The Hampshire
and Isle of Wight
Weather Book

Everybody is fascinated by the ever-changing moods of the weather and the patterns of the sky. Our climate is a perpetual talking point, particularly in the days of great floods and freezes, tempests and tornadoes, deluges, dust-devils and droughts. hailstones and heatwaves. In recent years, Hampshire and the Isle of Wight have experienced all these variations. The sheer intensity of rain has turned quiet rivers into raging torrents, a clash of air masses has led to a spectacular snowstorm, global warming has been blamed for the longest drought in history, tidal waves, 20 feet high, have pounded the coast, a jet aircraft has aquaplaned onto a motorway and opposing air streams have twice brought hurricane-force winds to change the face of the landscape. There has been more — much more — and, in this unique pictorial record of the weather in Hampshire and the Isle of Wight, we have the evidence.

Mark Davison, Ian Currie and Bob Ogley

Froglets Publications
and Frosted Earth

Froglets Publications Ltd, Brasted Chart, Westerham, Kent TN16 1LY.
Tel: 0959 562972 Fax 0959 565365

© 1993

Mark Davison, Ian Currie and Bob Ogley

ISBN 1 872337 20 1

Cover illustrations

Front cover: A motor car abandoned near Lyndhurst during the great snowstorm of December, 1937. Photograph by Topham Picture Source.

Back cover: Old Portsmouth Harbour, January 1993. By courtesy of The News, Portsmouth.

This book was originated by Froglets Publications Ltd., printed and bound by Staples Printers Rochester Ltd, Neptune Close, Medway City Estate, Rochester, Kent ME2 4LT.

Jacket design by Alison Stammers

ACKNOWLEDGEMENTS

IN the summer of 1992, through local newspapers in Hampshire and the Isle of Wight, we appealed for assistance in our research into dramatic weather events in the two counties. We also spoke on local radio, described our proposed book and invited the help of listeners. The response was fantastic. From Basingstoke to Bembridge, from Fordingbridge to Fareham came anecdotes, reminiscences, newspaper clippings and, in many cases, a photograph. Weather folklore came to light in dusty cellars and attics, confirming what we already knew about the great variety of weather in southern England.

We are grateful to all those who responded so enthusiastically and would particularly like to thank the staff of libraries and museums, editors and photographers of local newspapers, meteorologists, historians and all those who have given so much valued advice.

We thank the editorial and photographic staff of the Portsmouth News, Southern Evening Echo, Hampshire Chronicle, Bournemouth Echo, Basingstoke Gazette, Petersfield News, Alton Herald, Aldershot News, Isle of Wight County Press and the Hampshire County Magazine. They have provided a treasure chest of photographic memorabilia.

We are indebted to The Climatological Observers Link, The Royal Meteorological Society, Meteorological Office, Bracknell, Beaulieu Motor Museum, Hampshire County Council, Hampshire County Library, Dorset County Library, The Hampshire County Museum Service at Winchester, D-Day Museum, The Hampshire Fire Brigade, Isle of Wight County Record Office, Imperial War Museum Department of Photographs, The National Railway Museum, University of Dundee (Department of Electrical Engineering), The Longshoreman's Museum, Ventnor, Tornado and Storm Research Organisation, Curtis Museum, Alton, Venturers Search and Rescue.

Special thanks go to the following people, Mrs Christine Broom, Miss Jean Bowden, curator of the Jane Austen Memorial Trust, Kenneth Hosking, Colin Andrew, Ernest Cousins, Debbie King, Bert Broom, Mary Bryant, Mike Rowe (Torro), Pat Crossley, Sheila Ballantyne, Susan Tomkins, Mrs N.E. Mees, Mrs K.W. Harrison, C.D. Webster, A.M. Edmunds, Mrs Connie Hooker, A. G. McGregor, Dr Peter Smith, Timothy Butler, Philip and Marion Butler, R.J. Leary, Captain P.G. Pearce-Smith, Peter J. Legg, Mrs A. Harley, Stella Jarvis, R. Travers-Bogusz, L. C. Giles, Mrs Jan Willemstyn, G. Samuel, B. Ellis, Mrs K. Batchelor, D. and J. Blundell, Mrs Elsie Lee, Chris Hall, H.A. Richards, Leslie Herbert Gustar and the Gustar family, Brenda Jacobs, Phillipa Stevens, Carol Crossland, Alys Blakeway, Maureen Gale, Wendy Bell and Carol Morgan.

We consulted many books, notably Symons' British Railway, the Journal of Meteorology, The Weather of Britain, by Robin Stirling, Isle of Wight Shipwrecks and The Great Storm of 1987 published by the Portsmouth News.

The Hampshire and Isle of Wight Weather Book is the sixth of a county series of dramatic weather events and the others are available through bookshops or the publishers (see page 168). As with all of our books we are indebted to Mr Brian Girling for allowing us access to his wonderful postcard collection.

The map shows the two counties of Hampshire and the Isle of Wight together with the towns of Bournemouth, Christchurch and district which were part of Hampshire before boundary reorganisation placed them in the county of Dorset.

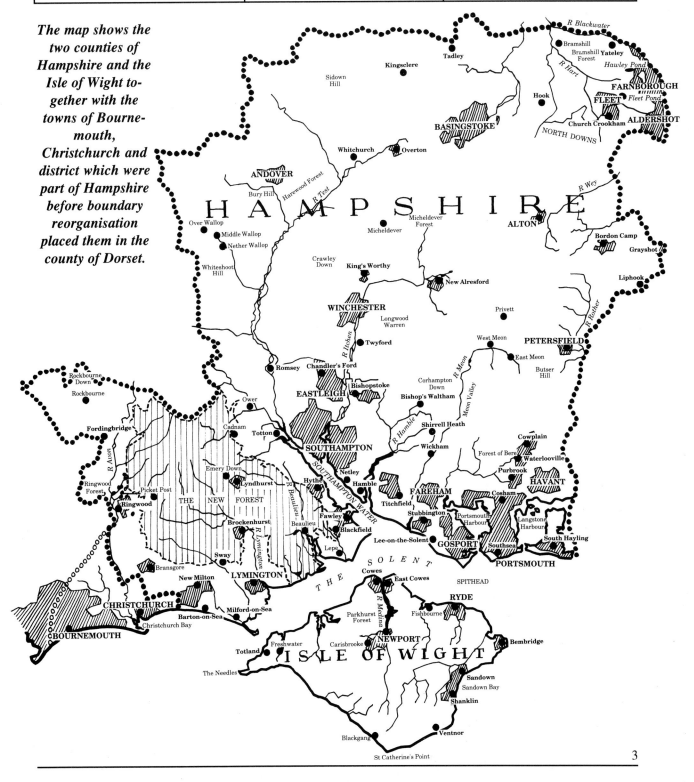

Great conflicts with the weather

GILBERT WHITE, one of Hampshire's most famous denizens, once described Selborne as an assemblage of hill, dale, woodland, heath and water — a description that can readily be applied to the rest of the county, and the Isle of Wight.

Over the centuries many battles have been fought on its soil but one of the greatest conflicts of all has been with the weather. Opposing winds have waged war from Ringwood to Havant and from Fleet to The Needles. One such battle began on Boxing Day, 1927. It lasted well into the New Year when rural communites were isolated by mountainous snowdrifts.

Another momentous occasion was in January 1881 when a clash of air masses led to a spectacular blizzard which buried the Isle of Wight under waist-deep snow and blew the tiny grains with such force that they penetrated through the smallest nooks and crannies into people's cottages.

Climate is not unalterable. When the Ice Age relaxed, the sea levels rose and the shape of Hampshire evolved. As the chalk hills were breached, the Solent, Southampton Water and Spithead were formed. Many scientists agree that the world is now warming up so the climate is likely to continue to change. It may be no coincidence that from 1988 to 1992, Hampshire endured the worst drought since the 1740s.

Hampshire is far enought east, away from the cloud and rain that often fringes the Atlantic coast, to share in some of the notable droughts. The worst was in 1921 when, around Portsmouth, rainfall was little more than that which falls in an average year on Alice Springs in the middle of the Australian desert. Indeed, the very desert descended upon town and country on lst July 1968 as Saharan dust coated newly-washed cars in an unwelcome multi-coloured display.

Sheltered by the South Downs, some parts of the county can become surprisingly warm. Around the head of Southampton Water in the hot summer of 1976, Mayflower Park eclipsed all previous heat records for June. Yet the same area in the bitter winter of 1963 brought scenes reminiscent of an Arctic shore with pack ice extending well out into the Solent.

Sunshine is no stranger to Hampshire and particularly to the Isle of Wight, often dubbed "Vectis, Britain's sunniest isle". There is some justification for this — an average of 1,858 hours of sunshine are recorded annually and that is more than 300 hours in excess of London or Cambridge.

However, these golden rays soaked up by the holidaymaker, often bring torment and frustration for the firefighter. The sandy heathlands around Aldershot, with their wisps of pine and birch, or the woody dells and heathery tracts of William the Conquerer's New Forest, can be the scenes of great blazes in sun-baked summers such as 1976 or 1990.

The former year saw patients being wheeled to safety from a hospital near Ringwood as windswept flames threatened to engulf it.

GOD'S PORT

Henry de Blois, who was among the most influential men in the country in the mid-12th century, almost lost his life in a great storm which raged throughout southern England in the winter of 1140 (exact date unknown). Henry, brother of King Stephen and grandson of the Conqueror, was sailing up the Solent when the wind and sea caused his ship to founder. The shore was not far away and, with great difficulty, Henry and his men managed to reach dry land.

Henry de Blois was also Bishop of Winchester and firmly believed he had been saved by God. He proclaimed the land on which he stood to be God's Port. So Gosport was named.

STORM QUEEN

Margaret, the young daughter of René of Anjou, was sailing to Portsmouth to meet her husband-to-be, King Henry Vl on 9th April, 1445 when a "terrific thunderstorm broke out". She landed at Portchester with the storm still raging, but loyal villagers "strewed the streets with rushes and cheered loudly".

The violence of the storm must have affected her health for the princess became ill, recovering in time for the marriage service at Titchfield Abbey on 22nd April. The wedding, of course, had been arranged. Henry Vl was 24 at the time and this was his first bride. Margaret was crowned Queen of England in May 1445.

Chapter One: 1600 — 1800

Wicked winters of long ago

1627: Two silver-laden ships came to grief near the Needles, Isle of Wight while trying to shelter from a howling south-westerly gale. The *Flying Dragon* and the *Campen*, part of a Dutch fleet, endeavoured to negotiate the narrow sea passage between the rocks, despite the sea spray blown up by the storm. The *Flying Dragon* was damaged but limped into The Solent where she was grounded. The *Campen* was smashed to pieces and the cargo of silver coins sank to the sea bed.

1648: The Isle of Wight suffered a dismal summer. A contemporary diary stated: "This Sommer of the Kinges beinge here 1648 wase more like winter then Sommer....In 40 years I never knew the like before, wee had scarse three drie dayes togeather but rayne hygh windes and stormes. In August we had not one drye daye, so that the corne wase like to rotte in ye ground."

1684: Probably the coldest winter Hampshire had known. The sea froze across at Southampton Water and, inland, couriers were frozen to death. The parish register of Holy Rood Church, Southampton says: "This yeare was a great Frost, which began before Christmasse, soe that ye river of Southampton was frossen all over and covered with ice from Calshott Castle to Redbridge". It adds that one man went on foot from his ice-bound vessel from Beray, near Marchwood to Millbrook Point. "Ye river at Itchen Berry was so frossen over that severall persons went from Beauvais Hill to Bitterne Farme, forwards and backwards."

Although the waters in Stuart times were shallower than now, and much wider, they were very much subject to the tides and the extent of icing during this winter was unprecedented. Sea ice was reported at other south coast locations. Polar ice was swept south from the Arctic by persistent northerly winds, and miniature ice-bergs massed together in the Dover Straits, closing the sea port of Southampton for some days.

Couriers heading out of London towards Salisbury were frozen to death, some within a short distance of Stockbridge. On 23rd December, 1684, a bone-chilling north-easterly wind whipped up snow into a blizzard. Snow mounted into huge drifts, some "as high as house tops". Roads familiar to the carriers became unrecognisable and the riders and their horses wandered around dazed and benumbed, some ending up miles off the beaten track, where they perished. One courier lost the use of his hands due to the severity of the cold near Stockbridge and his horses expired. The Exeter carrier also became hopelessly lost but miraculously survived the ordeal. The Wells carrier lost two passengers, his son aged about 13 and a young man of 20. They were both frozen to death.

1768: Gilbert White of Selborne wrote that between 3rd and 9th January it was so cold that the meat was frozen too hard to be spitted. Several types of thrushes were found frozen to death.

1776: January was one of the coldest ever recorded in Hampshire. On 31st, Gilbert White measured a

A light breeze and the Mary Rose sinks

IN July, 1545, King Henry VIII's great ship, the *Mary Rose*, turned turtle in Portsmouth Sound and sank with a loss of 650 men. With 60 other vessels she was preparing to meet the French fleet, anchored off the coast of the Isle of Wight — but the reason for her demise was a mystery.

Historians believe it may have been a combination of poor seamanship, a fault in the design of the ship in that open gunports were too near the water line, overloading with armoured soldiers and, of course, the weather. Although the sea had been calm, a light breeze sprang up and as she began to hoist sail, the *Mary Rose* was seen to get into difficulties. As she keeled to one side, her guns must have broken loose from their moorings and careered across the gun deck, adding their deadly weight to the ship's list to starboard. As she went down, the King's party watching from Southsea Castle heard the cries of the drowning men. Only 40 of the 650 men on the vessel survived.

As the years went by, Portsmouth did not forget the *Mary Rose*. Although she was invisible under the mud, except for the exposure of timbers when freak tides scoured the sea bed, the fishermen knew a good catch could be found near her grave. But there she lay, undisturbed for 437 years.

The Portsmouth Town Hall and Market Place in the summer of 1739 just before the most severe winter of the eighteenth century when the sea froze and "a gale blew straight from the heart of Russia". In those days the town hall was situated in the middle of the High Street but it caused so much obstruction to horse-drawn traffic that it was pulled down in 1837.

1600 — 1800 (cont)

temperature of 0F (-18C) just before sunrise. "With rime on the trees and on the tube of the glass, the quicksilver sunk exactly to zero. The birds now began to be in a very pitiable and starving condition. Tamed by the season, skylarks settled in the streets of towns because they saw the ground was bare; rooks frequented dunghills close to houses; crows watched horses as they passed and greedily devoured what dropped from them; hares came into men's gardens and, scraping away the snow, devoured such plants as they could find".

The Itchen, Hamble and Bursledon rivers were completely frozen and, at Southampton, there was a solid mass of ice from Watergate Key to Redbridge. A carter who lost his way at Winchester was found frozen to death while a manservant, who was missing for two days, was found buried in snow only 300 yards from his master's house.

So terrible was the weather that Southampton Corporation opened a subscription for the relief of the starving. Gilbert White noted that it was so cold that ice formed under beds and in warm chambers. "In the day, wind was so keen that persons of robust constitutions could scarcely endure to face it. The dry, powdery snow lay for 26 days on roofs and turned grey with the dust. By the time the thaw came in early February, the thrushes and blackbirds were mostly destroyed".

1777: At the end of July "such vast rains fell about Iping, Bramshot and Haslemere that they tore vast holes in the turnpike roads and covered meadows with sand. Near Haslemere, a post boy drowned".

1783: During a violent storm at Winchester on 10th July, a prisoner "who had been boasting of his eyes and profanely swearing that they were not to be dazzled by the strongest flashes, was suddenly struck stone-blind by lightning. Notwithstanding, every medical effort was employed but there was no hope of his recovering his sight".

A long range forecast, but is it true?

St Swithin's Day, if thou dost rain
For forty days it will remain
St Swithin's Day, if thou be fair
For forty days 'twill rain nae mair.

THIS is a legend that everyone knows and no-one believes. There is certainly no record of rain falling for 40 consecutive days in modern times and it is unlikely that it has ever occurred.

Swithin was a ninth century monk who became Bishop of Winchester in 852 and held the post until his death 10 years later. He was a pious, self effacing man by all accounts, particularly active in restoring churches. On his death bed he requested to be buried, not within the cathedral but outside in a "vile and unworthy place un-der the drips of eaves". Bishop Swithin wanted the "sweet rain of heaven" to fall on his grave.

About 100 years later the clergy at Winchester decided to transfer his remains to a tomb in a new church and a grand ceremony was held on 15th July. As the pomp was about to commence, so the legend states, a terrific storm raged and it began to rain heavily, continuing without a break for forty days. Hence the superstition.

Studies carried out in London have shown that the longest spell of consecutive wet days after St Swithin's Day was in 1939 when 15th July was bone dry. This famous long-range weather forecast is not accurate.

1786: During a south-easterly storm on 9th December, a 900-ton Dutch frigate was wrecked at Sudmoor Point, Isle of Wight. Six of her crew were drowned and the ship was a complete loss.

1788: A land devil — or whirlwind — blew up straw and garden debris at Farringdon on 21st April and took away two rooks' nests carrying young squabs, according to Gilbert White.

1790: New Year's Day "more the influence of May than January" according to the *Hampshire Chronicle*. A nightingale was heard on the South Coast. On 23rd December, thunder, rain and snow damaged ships at Portsmouth.

1798-9: About a dozen crew members of the ship, *Henry Addington*, were drowned when she was wrecked during a thick winter fog. In January, the West Indiaman, *Three Sisters* was caught in a thunderstorm while attempting to reach Portsmouth. The crew were overwhelmed by snow and rain and three drowned at Puckaster Cove, Niton on the Isle of Wight's south coast. Deep snowdrifts formed on the island and carriages had to be dug out from many places between Newport and Ryde, and at Cowes. Three people were found frozen to death on the Downs and at Chale Common.

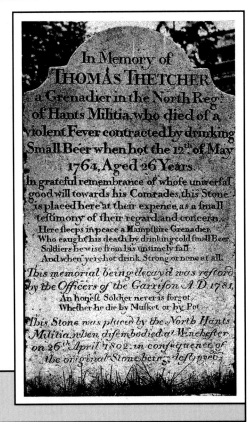

The hot weather on 12th May, 1764 must have been exceptional for it killed this man who drank small beer! The information was found on his tombstone.

Tempest claims 8,000 lives

26th November, 1703

"NO pen could describe it, nor tongue express it, nor thought conceive it unless by one in the extremity of it." These were Daniel Defoe's words about what was arguably the greatest storm of all — and Hampshire stood full square in its path. From midnight until dawn a "perfect hurricane" raged across the south of England, such that in the grey and feeble first light "nobody could believe the hundreth part they saw".

Many buildings were in ruins, streets were deep in fallen masonry and thousands of trees strewn about. Church steeples lay prostrate on the ground, over 400 windmills were smashed and the newly-constructed Eddystone Lighthouse was demolished. Ironically, its creator and builder, Henry Winstanley was in residence "to see what effect the storm would have on his building". He was killed.

This night of violence followed a series of gales which had swept Britain for a week from 19th November. A deepening low crossed the Midlands with fierce winds on its southern flanks. Defoe's own barometer read a value so low he thought children had broken it. The booming roar of the wind outside became all-pervading and it was estimated that it reached 120 mph. Even such well-built edifices as Christchurch Priory and the vicarage at Hartley Wintney succumbed. Buildings crashed down in Ringwood, Fordingbridge and Basingstoke.

On the Isle of Wight, spray from the tumultuous seas covered fields with a snow-like encrustation of salt rendering whole pastures inedible to sheep and cattle. Thousands of trees toppled in the New Forest. In Selborne, later to become immortalised by the naturalist, Gilbert White, the great oak was struck down which had stood in the Plestor for 400 years since its planting in the reign of Henry III. White later wrote, "This vast oak surrounded with stone steps and seats above them, was the delight of old and young, and a place of much resort in summer evenings. Long might it have stood, had not the amazing tempest of 1703 overturned it at once."

The coastal towns "looked as if the enemy had sackt them and were most miserably torn to pieces". Dozens of dwelling places lay in ruin. At Lymington, the centre of an important salt trade, where both natural and artificial salt were manufactured, the sea swept over Hurst Beach ruining many of the salterns. It was two years before full production could be resumed.

It is scarcely possible to imagine the appalling state of the sea and the terrifying nature of those hellish winds. Britain was engaged in the War of the Spanish Succession and three fleets were assembled to aid the King of Spain against the French. Off Cowes and Portsmouth these mighty vessels lay at anchor along with attendant merchantmen and storeships. In the maelstrom brought about by the combined effects of hurricane-force winds, tides and the turbulent nature of the waters, due to the confines of the Channel between the island and the mainland, ships were scattered and overwhelmed.

Daylight revealed a mass of stricken vessels in The Solent and Spithead. One

Daniel Defoe — "nobody could believe the hundreth part they saw".

boat was even torn from moorings on the Helford River in Cornwall only to become firmly wedged onto rocks at St Helens, south of Bembridge. Estimates put the loss of life at sea as high as 15,000 whereas Daniel Defoe in his book thought it to be a more modest 8,000. Nonetheless it meant the Navy had to press new men into service, often by dubious methods including the pardoning of convicted criminals awaiting the gallows. Even on land, fatalities amounted to more than 100, including the Bishop of Bath and Wells, crushed by a falling chimney as he slept.

There were those who profited from the event and none more so than the tilers, bricklayers and glaziers whose wages trebled. Hardly one house in Hampshire was spared damage.

In London, Queen Anne sheltered in a cellar under St James' Palace as chimneys toppled and part of the roof gave way. She was later to issue a proclamation for a national day of fast on 19th January, 1704 to pay respects to the privations and loss of life suffered by her subjects. In the parish register of St Michael's Church, Southampton, these words provide a clear summary of the events: "A dreadful storm of wind happened in England and many other parts of the World the 26th day and 27th day of November, 1703 in the evening and continued till next morning which beat down many stacks of chimneys and houses and abundance of trees blown down by the root and many ships at sea lost which was thought to be the greatest storm that ever happened".

The south view of Selborne Church and the famous yew.

Gilbert White and the Selborne Yew

THE great tempest of 1703 may have felled Henry III's magnificent oak but it caused little damage to the Great Yew of Selborne* which was then about 1,200 years old and one of the most famous trees in England. Historians believe that the yew began life about the time of the conversion of Wessex to Christianity and may have been planted as a symbol of immortality — respect for the tree having been taken over from pre-Christian times when sacred trees were venerated.

One man who knew the Great Yew well was the naturalist Gilbert White, born in 1720 in the vicarage in Selborne. He provided the subject matter for a book which has become a classic of English writing, *The Natural History and Antiquities of Selborne.*

White wrote as follows: "In the churchyard of this village is a yew-tree whose aspect bespeaks it to be of great age: it seems to have seen several centuries, and is probably coeval with the church, and therefore may be deemed an antiquity: the body is squat, short and thick, and measures 23 feet in girth, supporting an head of suitable extent in its bulk. This is a male tree, which in the spring sheds clouds of dust and fills the atmosphere with its farina."

The Reverend White — having become curate at Selborne — frequently mentioned the weather in his writings. "I well remember that after the severe spring of 1740, summer birds of passage were very scarce....In that unfavourable year the winds blowed the whole spring and summer through from opposite quarters".

He wrote about the "portentuous" summer of 1783 which was full of "horrible phaenomena" for..."besides the alarming meteors and tremendous thunderstorms that affrightened and distressed, the peculiar haze, of smokey fog that prevailed was unlike anything known in the memory of man".

A year later he described the thunderstorm of 5th June, 1784 which "began in the parish of Hartley with vast drops of rain which were soon succeeded by round hail and then by convex pieces of ice which measured three inches in girth. There fell at the same time prodigious torrents of rain which occasioned a flood as violent as it was sudden; doing great damage to the meadows and fallows, by deluging the one and washing away the soil of the other. The hollow lane towards Alton was so torn and disordered as not to be passable till mended, rocks being removed that weighed 200 weight".

Gilbert White was also the first to discover frost hollows and his experiments with barometers between Selborne and Newton Valence showed that air pressure lowered with height. He died in Selborne at his home The Wakes on 26th June, 1793 aged 72.

* The Selborne Yew survived until the afternoon of 25th January, 1990, when in another great storm it was torn up by its roots. *See page 152*

When defeat was glorious

HAMPSHIRE, well known for its temperate climate, has a yearly rainfall that is less than the national average and a sunshine record that annually exceeds 1,600 hours. Because of the many springs hidden under the chalk, the county seldom suffers from drought conditions that can be so critical to other areas. Little wonder then that Hampshire supports thriving vineyards, and watercress beds that account for half the country's market, while the long growing season provides a wide choice of quality vegetables, fruit and flowers.

Near the eastern coastline, the villages around Titchfield, Swanwick, Sarisbury and Lock's Heath boast such wonderful early summer conditions that it has become the most famous strawberry growing area in the British Isles.

The clear and cool chalk, angling waters of the Meon, Itchen and Test also yield their own produce, including salmon and trout. The River Test is reputedly the finest trout stream of its kind in the world, fed by springs under the chalk and the "capital" of the Test Valley is Stockbridge, heart of the fishing country.

There is another summer sport which owes much to the county of Hampshire — cricket. Broad Halfpenny Down has been described as the birthplace of the modern game. Certainly Hambledon was the best-known team in England, pitting their skills against all-England at the end of the eighteenth century and inducing crowds to flock to Broad Halfpenny Down on those balmy summer days.

This flat table of turf set in the Hampshire Downland, overlooked by a rustic pub and a thatched pavilion, stands supreme as the cradle of modern cricket. Each blade of grass and each leaf which rustles in the breeze holds the memory of low cunning and inspired genius, obsessive daftness and enchanting poetry. These Hambledon men took rough clubs, crude stumps and painstakingly forged, from a mixture of make-believe and mayhem, the great noble and incredible ritual which we call cricket.

On those glorious summer days, the might of Hambledon smote and flailed the men from all of England. They played out an ancient magic, long sleeping in the weathered turf.

John Nyren, son of one of the village heroes wrote a most evocative book about the game in Hambledon. "Oh it was a heart-stirring sight to witness the multitude forming a complete and dense circle round that noble green. Half the county would be present and all their hearts with us. Defeat was glory in such a struggle — Victory indeed made us only a little lower than angels."

A modern cricket match on the less-breezy Windmill Down, which has become the home for Hambledon CC. In 1992, the club was not the champion of all-England, but they won the Hampshire League championship in great style.

Chapter Two: 1800 — 1900

Troubled years for turnips

1810: A tornado left a trail of havoc around Portsmouth on 14th December. The *Gentleman's Magazine* reported: "At Southsea Common, four houses were levelled to the ground, and as many so much injured as to render it necessary to take them down; besides 30 others unroofed." There was great damage at Southampton, Portsmouth and Cowes.

Another tornado struck the Ringwood district. The *Hampshire Telegraph* said: "A similar tornado to that which was felt at Portsmouth was experienced at Fordingbridge. The lead of the church in many parts was rolled up like rolls of floor cloth and several houses were unroofed.

1814: A severe spell of cold and snow. There was "a complete stoppage" on some roads near Yateley. At Hindhead, and on the hills of Hampshire, the snow had drifted to 15 feet deep and some parts of the West Country had the deepest snow for at least 40 years. January was one of the coldest of the 19th century.

1815: A dry, hot summer. At Broughton, farmer Hinton Bailey wrote: "A most remarkable summer, extremely hot and dry from about the middle of June to 20th September — a period of nearly three months without scarcely a shower of rain. No turnips on the light soils, yet the sheep did remarkably well".

1816: A cold and backward spring. Farmer Bailey wrote that rain fell continually in the Test Valley from the middle of June to 24th August. A violent storm hit Winchester in May. Harvesting could not begin until 14th August, one of the latest dates of the 19th century, and was not completed until 14th October — and, at Winchester, the middle of November.

1820: Severe winter weather gripped the county during the first three weeks of January with a penetrating and intense frost on the 13th. Thick snow lay on the Isle of Wight. A violent storm struck Newport in early August. The eclipse of the sun was observed from Gosport in September.

> A thunderstorm ravaged Alresford and vicinity on 20th December, 1820 during which a waterspout was seen — a rare occurrence on land. According to the *Reading Mercury*, it moved with great velocity and its course was serpentine. It lasted two minutes and its principal fury was "expended upon a farmhouse and some hovels in Ropley". Although it was described as a water spout, it was not attended with any discharge of water and therefore was more likely to have been a tornado.

1821: A wet and cold summer dampened the spirits of Hampshire farmers. A tremendous hailstorm battered Shirley in early April and later in the month a storm blew up at Newport. On 27th May it snowed so much that three inches lay on the road between Fareham and Winchester.

1822: Farmers near Stockbridge reported "the mildest and wettest winter ever" with no ice during winter or spring. A severe July storm battered the south coast at Southampton and Portsmouth.

1823: A severe frost occurred in the Test Valley on the night of the longest day which destroyed many vegetables. There was also a big frost on midsummer's morning at Newport.

1824: Violent winds caused structural damage in Winchester in November. An earth tremor was reported in the Emsworth area in December.

1826: A remarkable summer for lack of rain which lasted from the first week of March to the end of August. Berry Court Farm, Nether Wallop reported a "lamentable deficiency at harvest — oats a total failure and no turnips at all". A lunar eclipse was seen from Gosport in November.

1828: An unusually mild winter and advanced spring but the "wettest summer in recollection". Storms in January caused damage in Southampton and other towns. There was a "violent hurricane" in Winchester in early September.

1829: A summer storm drove the full-rigged East Indiaman *Carn Brae Castle* ashore on 5th July. Her hull was split as she hit rocks at Brook Ledge and, in appalling conditions, rescues were attempted by local fishing boats. It was the greatest shipwreck of the 1820s around the Isle of Wight. Cold weather set in before Christmas with severe frosts and snow. By 28th December, the churchwardens of Westbourne had collected enough firewood to supply 300 poor families with the comfort "of at least a fortnight's fire".

1830: Another severe winter with snow on the ground from December to February. The *Hampshire Telegraph* reported that every sheet of ice in the Test Valley was daily thronged with skaters. By 11th January the poor people of Petersfield had been given "three fat oxen and a liberal supply of soup by Sir Harry Featherstone of Uppark. At Southampton the river froze from shore to shore for the first time in anyone's memory. February brought a rapid thaw.

Twenty people died when The Clarendon went down

Clarendon sinks in a blizzard

1836: On 11th October, a gale of "hurricane force" caused *The Clarendon* to take in water and sink near the south-west shore of the Isle of Wight. With a crew of 13 and 10 passengers plus a cargo of rum, sugar, arrowroot, coconuts and turtles from the West Indies, *The Clarendon* was driven inland and broke into pieces. Islanders made a dramatic rescue bid but to no avail. Only 3 seamen survived.

The winter of 1836-7 had begun in October with sharp frosts and snow. England's first and only avalanche occurred on Christmas night at Lewes in Sussex when snow piled high on the Downs and then swept down, burying a number of cottages and killing eight people. This was followed by the severest and coldest spring "ever remembered".

1849: After a mild winter the weather fooled everyone in April when snow fell on the 19th. In Winchester it was very heavy and there was an inch on the ground at Southampton. The summer was "delightful in every respect" but in October, 2.1 inches of rain fell during a thunderstorm which provided vivid flashes of lightning all night.

1859: A mild winter in West Hampshire was followed by a warm and pleasant summer and then a "very severe frost on 24th October which caused the mangolds, turnips and swedes to rot and decay". October brought a tremendous gale which caused damage in Portsmouth, Ryde and Gosport. In December, the temperature fell to a numbing 9F (-13C).

Murphy got it right — then he got it wrong!

SEVERE weather set in after 5th January, 1838 — a year which was to be known as "Murphy's Winter", after the eccentric weather prophet. By 20th January it was so cold that some of Britain's lowest known temperatures occurred and, near Stockbridge, frost continued for seven weeks.

At Southampton, huge flocks of wildfowl were driven to the coastline in search of food. Skaters took to the ice at Newport, Isle of Wight in a spectacle that "presented a scene of gaiety,

closely resembling a Dutch Fair". At Basingstoke, the poor were given cash from the coal fund to help during "this unusually severe season" — a practice which was common all over the county.

This famous spell of Siberian weather was known as "Murphy's Winter" after the prophet had correctly foretold in his almanac that the coldest day of the winter would be on 20th January. He was hailed as a hero — until the following year, when he got it badly wrong!

Jane's affair with the Hampshire weather

JANE Austen who was born in the Hampshire village of Steventon, lived at Chawton with her mother and sister from 1809 until her early death in 1817. From this last house she completed *Mansfield Park, Emma* and *Persuasion.* She also wrote many letters to friends and relatives and commented frequently on the variety of the Hampshire weather.

In a letter dated **Sunday 20th November, 1808,** Jane asked her sister Cassandra: "How could you have had a wet day (at Godmersham Park in Kent) on Thursday? With us it was a Prince of days, the most delightful we have had for weeks, soft, bright, with a brisk wind from the south-west; everybody was out and talking of spring and Martha and I didn't know how to turn back......On Friday evening we had some very blowing weather — I think we never had it worse, even here. And one night we had so much rain that it forced its way again into the store closet — and tho' the Evil was compara-

tively slight and the Mischief nothing, I had some employment the next day in drying parcels etc.

On **4th February, 1814** (again to Cassandra): "I walked to Alton and, dirt excepted, found it delightful, it seemed like an old February come back again".

To her nephew, Edward, on Tuesday **9th July, 1816:** "It has been too bad for a long time, much worse than anyone can bear, and I begin to think it will never be fine again. This is a finesse of mine, for I have often observed that if one writes about the weather, it is generally changed before the letter is read...Oh! it rains again".

On **24th January, 1817** (the year she died), Jane wrote: "Such mild weather is, you know, delightful to us, and though we have a great many ponds, and a fine running stream through the meadows on the other side of the road, it is nothing but what beautifies us and does to talk of."

Sea claimed 'all Portsmouth'

4th-5th March, 1818

OLD newspapers tell of mighty gales, amazing frosts, of deluge, drought and even dust storms. But no account is more dramatic than that of 4th-5th March, 1818 when "the crust of all Europe faltered, not merely under dry land but under the sea as well and Hampshire and the Isle of Wight experienced a mighty tempest that lasted three terrible hours".

When it was all over and the Continental newspapers had reached Portsmouth, the *Hampshire Telegraph* quoted this passage from a Paris journal: "All over Europe the elements are at war. It seems as if a great physical revolution is in preparation. Luminous meteors discharge stones, earthquakes have been felt in all latitudes, waterspouts carry people up into the air, all the shores are covered with wrecks."

There were many harrowing events at sea and the *Telegraph* told of a passenger ship which ran into the tempest. "A ball of fire struck the sea within yards of the ship, throwing up water to a height of 40 feet. Part of the ball entered the cabin and killed a dog".

One of the heroes of the storm was a Portsmouth-based naval officer. The mail coach in which he was travelling home on leave was blown into a Wiltshire river. The officer rescued all the passengers and then, plunging back into the torrent, unharnessed the horses and guided them to the bank.

The gale hit Portsmouth a few hours before high tide was due and the force of the wind drove the flood tide towards Portsea Island. "Leaping and swooping over the bulwark of the Isle of Wight, it piled the sea level even higher." The flood drove inshore and soon

the water was two feet deep in Broad Street. By 9 pm the sea had risen five feet above the level of normal spring tides and, at that level, stayed for more than three hours.

During that time all Portsmouth and the greater part of Portsea Island were flooded and, at Southsea, a mile-long breach was torn in the shingle bank. Horsea Island vanished under the waves and next morning the carcasses of dead sheep afforded plunder for villagers on the Portchester foreshore. The water squeezed through the narrow part of the harbour entrance and, between Round Tower and Point, swept entire buildings away.

On the Isle of Wight, in the lower part of Ryde and Cowes, the invading sea battered down front doors and swept away staircases. Ryde's new pier was demolished. Thirty six of its 40 great timber arches were torn adrift and washed ashore at Hayling and Southsea.

After the dreadful events, this advertisement in the *Telegraph* appealed for help: "Drowned on Wednesday evening by the upsetting of a wherry in the Mouth of the Harbour — Mr Hassall, Mr Thellusson and Mr Leeson, all dressed in Midshipmen's Uniform. Whoever may find the bodies of the Young Gentlemen, and will give information of the same to Messrs Mottley and Harrison, shall receive a reward of FIVE POUNDS for each body".

Later writers suggested that a logical explanation of the disaster was that, with the upheaval on the sea bed, a tidal wave had occurred. Almost simultaneously the tempest burst from the south "driving the huge wall of water to pounce on such sitting ducks as low-lying Portsea Island."

1800 — 1900 (cont)

When the willow bloomed in February

1860: A severe winter, a wet and cold spring and a miserable summer in which wheat was "the worst in quantity ever recollected". At Havant, the corn could not be cut until September. Christmas Day had an iron frost with a temperature of 10F (-12C) recorded at Southampton. This was followed by snow and terrible flooding, particularly at Wallington.

1863: At Selborne, the willow was in bloom on 15th February. There was a total eclipse of the moon on 1st June. July was warm and harvest time in August was "delightful". At the end of November a whirlwind occurred in Winchester.

1865: There were damaging gales in Portsmouth in January during an unusually snowy winter. The ice, over a large stretch of the river near Houghton Mill, had to be broken to keep the mill wheel turning. April made amends for the cold winter with temperatures climbing to 79F (26C) on the 26th and 27th.

1866: Many boats were wrecked during a fierce gale in February, including those sheltering in Studland Bay, Bournemouth. At Cadland, Southampton, 12 inches of rain fell during January and February. During the year, it rained on 199 days.

1867: Queen Victoria went out on a sledge while staying at Osborne House, Isle of Wight and, at Sandown, 80 people enjoyed skating and hockey on the ice at the waterworks. On 4th January, the temperature fell to a bone-chilling 4F (-15C) in Southampton, causing great distress. During the daytime it reached only 19.5F ((-7C) at Selborne. At Chawton, near Alton there were reports of a temperature as low as -5F (-21C), making it one of the coldest nights ever known. The postman on the Winchester-Stockbridge route had to walk his horse eight miles to Stockbridge each night because it was too hazardous to ride. The London to Salisbury train was stuck fast for 12 hours after great walls of snow crashed down on the track at Andover. Bournemouth Pier was badly damaged in a gale on 5th January and five vessels were blown on shore.

1868: Hay was being cut in the park at Selborne by 10th June and haymaking was completed by 17th June. Some of Britain's hottest ever temperatures occurred on 22nd July. Parts of Hampshire reported readings in excess of 95F (35C) during the month.

Professor Thomas Bell of Selborne, who kept a diary, recording some of the dramatic weather events in Hampshire

1870: Roads were icebound on the Isle of Wight for weeks during February, which was bitterly cold. There was a landslide near Rock End, St Lawrence in which a house slipped into the sea. Biting winds blew from the north-east.

1872: A heavy thunderstorm broke at Selborne on 25th July and lasted for three hours, releasing 1.5 inches of rain. Properties at Havant were flooded and a house at Selborne was struck by lightning. At Alton, the annual rainfall totalled 48 inches.

1873: A generally dry year was broken by a notable downpour on 13th July. Weather diarist Professor. Thomas Bell of Selborne measured 2.16 inches (55mm) and the barometer fell to 28.94 inches. There was so much snow at Havant on 12th December that carts could not be driven.

1874: A "second summer" occurred in October but two months later it was bitterly cold. Professor Bell recorded a minimum temperature of 8F (-13C) on the morning of New Year's Eve and by 6 pm it was down to 6F (-14C) while at at East Tisted 3F (-16C) was measured.

1877: The year was remembered for its violent storm on New Year's Day followed by more gales towards the end of January. Diarist Martha Burrows wrote about "ten weeks of rain" at Havant during which the Lavant Brook came into North Street, flooding all the houses.

1878: Earthquake tremors were reported in Southampton early in the year. Gosport weathermen reported a violent storm in May, a month in which a waterspout was seen near Ryde A very icy winter..

continued on page 18

On a warm Saturday evening during the summer of 1867, a solicitor's clerk and former Sunday school teacher penned an extraordinary entry in the diary he kept among the legal papers at his office in Alton. Under the date, 24th August, he wrote: "Killed a young girl. It was fine and hot".

The girl was Fanny Adams, an eight-year-old who had left her house in Tanhouse Lane to play in Flood Meadow with her younger sister, Lizzie and her friend Minnie Warner. There they met the clerk, Frederick Baker, who picked Fanny up, carried her into a nearby hopfield and brutally hacked her to death. He was quickly found, charged, convicted and hanged a few months later at Winchester.

The incident shocked the people of Alton who could not understand what motives there could have been for such a brutal murder of a child, simply known as "Sweet Fanny Adams". See page 28.

The old wooden pier at Bournemouth, built at a cost of £4,000 and opened in September, 1861, was another victim of the weather. Weakened by teredo, or shipworm, which attacked the piles, it became easy prey to gales and heavy seas. The head of the pier was demolished in "a hurricane" in January, 1867 and the main structure collapsed in another severe storm in November 1876. It was replaced by an entirely new structure — 838 feet long and 110 feet wide, costing the then enormous sum of £21,000. In the coming years there were many new additions including a clock, covered shelters, bandstand, electric lighting, landing stage and pier theatre. Picture shows the old pier shortly after its opening in 1861.

15 blissful summer years at Osborne

IT was the agreeable climate of the Isle of Wight and the great desire for a small, cosy and secluded place which persuaded Queen Victoria and Prince Albert to buy Osborne House, near Cowes and so "indulge in the same simple recreations as ordinary people". The couple moved in during the very warm September 1846 and, 'were blissfully happy'.

With Buckingham Palace, Windsor Castle, the Pavilion at Brighton and Claremont at Esher, Victoria and Albert could hardly complain that they had a housing problem. But Osborne was a favourite holiday retreat. Their nine children — four boys and five girls — spent the long summer days catching butterflies while Victoria rested in the shadow of the trees, well away from the affairs of State and Albert

laid out the plantations and displayed his talents as farmer, forester and gardener. Fifteen eventful years passed and then tragedy struck.

In the wet and col8 November, 1861 an outbreak of typhoid fever spread from Portugal to England; the Prince fell victim to it and for three weeks lay dangerously ill. Everything within the limits of contemporary medical knowledge was done for him, but on 14th December, 1861, he died.

The Queen's grief was overwhelming. For another 40 years she remained a widow — mostly at Osborne — acting the role of Queen of England and Empress of India in lonely dignity. She died at Osborne, aged 81, on 22nd January, 1901. So ended, not only a life but an entire age.

The Globe Hotel, Cowes which was almost destroyed by the tornado.

Cowes battered by tornado

28th September, 1876

THE maritime community of Cowes on the northern tip of the Isle of Wight was torn apart by an incredible tornado which struck at breakfast time on 28th September, 1876.

At first light, before the whirlwind struck, people noticed a distinct heaviness of the atmosphere and, in the sky, a great number of birds flew about as if in alarm. Between seven and eight o'clock came a violent rushing wind in a north-easterly direction, parallel with the shore. It lasted only a few seconds and did not extend more than 100 feet in width, but in that short time and within that limited area, it accomplished unbelievable destruction.

Houses were unroofed, or blown down, large trees were torn apart, boats, high and dry on the shore were carried off to sea, "capsized and smashed to atoms" and the air was thick with flying branches, slates and other debris. The Globe and Marine Hotels were almost demolished and the whole town suffered very severely. Miraculously no-one was killed but a number of people were injured. At Mr Davis' farm in Broadfields, there were many buildings razed. Four men were buried beneath the rubble of a blown-down barn but, remarkably, they were rescued.

Eye witnesses spoke of scenes resembling a bombardment. "Stones were carried by the violence of the hurricane to vessels cruising in the Solent and the yacht *Lanola*, which was lying half a mile from shore, had a pan tile firmly embedded in her bulwarks." Cowes railway station was wrecked and many carriages damaged. The Old Promenade pier was a tangled mass of buckled railings, snapped timbers and boats.

Bridge demolished on Hayling Island

1st January, 1877

THIS New Year storm was ushered in by boisterous south-westerly winds which lashed the South Coast for two days causing widespread damage and misery to families, some of whom had to seek refuge in the top floors of their flooded homes.

The storm combined with an exceptionally high tide which sent massive waves crashing into town centres all along the Hampshire and Sussex coast. Southampton, particularly, was hard hit. Sea water invaded low-lying homes, thrusting its way through doors, demolishing walls and swirling into living rooms.

While poor families alongside the banks of the Itchen climbed stairs to escape the muddy torrents, those in Marine Parade made their getaway by boat. In the Glebe Road area, 26 garden walls were demolished by the water.

"Fowls, dogs, boxes of tools and household stuff were floating about in all directions", wrote the *Hampshire Independent*. "A woman narrowly escaped a falling wall as she was releasing her dog which was tied up."

At Northam, the Chapel was under two feet of water and boats were used to rescue livestock from fields which had turned into lakes. Around Redbridge, the causeway was under five feet of water and trees could be seen in the meadows sticking out of the floods. At Portsmouth, shingle was picked up by the waves and hurled at the windows of nearby homes. Broad Street, Southsea resembled a "bad imitation of the Grand Canal in Venice." The connecting bridge to Hayling Island was blown down and the island cut off from the mainland.

The Isle of Wight fared little better and, at Cowes, the tide was said to be the highest for 50 years.

1800 — 1900 (continued)

1879: This was a disastrous summer for farmers — cold, wet and sunless. Some parts of southern Britain suffered below-average temperatures for every month of the year. There were terrible floods during the summer which led to the loss of thousands of sheep. The year ended with a winter thunderstorm on 30th December with "unusually numerous hailstones and lightning exceedingly vivid". At Laverstoke on Christmas Eve, Lady Charlotte Peal dispensed beef to 150 families and 100 labourers which "went some way to alleviating their distress caused by the inclement weather".

1880: January was bitterly cold and a resident of Winchester wrote to the *Hampshire Chronicle*: "We are having some very sharp weather, more severe than is comfortable to us old folk, whose blood is losing its iron, notwithstanding the sufficiency to eat, with good fires and plenty of blankets. It must be a miserable time for the thousands amongst us who have scarcely one meal a day, a fireless hearth and scanty clothing."

1883: February was remarkably wet. At Alton, 6.63 inches fell during the month. In parts of Southern England, March was the coldest since 1845. There was a severe storm along the South Coast in November and a notable gale in December.

1885: A spring snowstorm raged across Hampshire on 22nd March, accompanied by high winds which blew down many telegraph poles. It was particularly bad in Havant. A great heat pushed the temperature up to a roasting 94.5 (34C) on 26th July on the Isle of Wight. It was hotter than anywhere in England on that day.

1886: A violent snowstorm took place on the night of 20th January and by 9 am only four children had turned up at Liphook School. "As the number had not improved by 9.30, school was closed for the day", according to the school logbook. At Odiham, said a contemporary report, "heavy snowstorms passed over this neighbourhood. Next day a thaw set in and from that time the streets were in a sloppy and most wretched state".

1887: January was a month of bitter cold and New Year's Day at Harestock, near Winchester saw the temperature as low as 15F (-10C). On the morning of Jubilee Day, 21st June, a frost was reported at Basingstoke with the air temperature at 34F (1C). July was glorious.

1888: A cold northerly airstream brought snow to Winchester on 12th July, although experts argue that it may have been a type of hail. In parts of the South, 11 out of 12 months of 1888 had below average temperatures.

1889: Another cold winter to start the year. Earthquake tremors were felt in Portsmouth in May.

Continued on p. 29

HMS Eurydice capsized off Dunnose Point, Ventnor, in a snow squall, losing 364 seamen.

364 seamen perish in a blizzard

22nd March, 1878

A SAVAGE snow squall on a cold, bright day in March 1878 led to the death of 364 seamen when the *HMS Eurydice* capsized on the last leg of her journey to Portsmouth.

It was a normal early spring afternoon in the English Channel. A fresh north-westerly wind was blowing, and despite some towering cumulus clouds, the sun shone on the Isle of Wight and Hampshire. Around 3.45 pm, the captain of a coal-bearing schooner, *The Emma*, noticed an awesome black sky growing menacingly across the northern skyline. Wisely he took precautions. Fishermen headed towards Culver Cliff, near Sandown Bay while Captain Jenkins reefed his sails.

Meanwhile, *Eurydice*, a 921 training frigate built in 1843, sailed on with the crew apparently taking no heed of the obvious warning the evil-looking sky was giving. Minutes later, the pent-up fury of the 30,000-foot cloud was unleashed on the Channel, in the form of thousands of tons of ice which could no longer be borne by the cloud.

The great squall enveloped the ship in a spectacular ice storm and, in those dramatic moments, the vessel was completely hidden from view. Realising the danger, the crew members climbed the nets and were almost blown off by the force of the wind. The taut sails quickly became filled with heavy snow and the frigate was rotated through 90 degrees to face south-east before being forced over onto her star-board side. Some of the top masts were wrenched away and, before long, the foaming sea started to flood through the open starboard port holes.

There were two survivors. One grabbed a lifebuoy and plunged into the icy water. The other climbed onto the portside of the hull as the ship capsized and hung on to the last moment before going into the sea. The *Eurydice* corrected herself in a last bid to defy the storm but then her bow was pushed mercilessly down and the vessel sank to the seabed.

In that sensational storm, which had brewed up on an airstream originating in the Arctic regions, many seamen tried to survive by peeling off their clothes and leaping into the sea. Although the winter had been a little milder than usual, the water was never-theless at its coldest after the winter months. In a few short moments the sea claimed the lives of all but two of those who dived off the stricken craft.

After 45 minutes the blizzard stopped and the sun appeared on the top sails of the *Eurydice*, which was all that could be seen above the waves.

Many years later, one of the two survivors admitted that the entire crew had been drinking heavily, presumably at the prospect of the ship returning home to Portsmouth after a long voyage around the West Indies. When snow gathered in the topsails and made the vessel top heavy, not one seaman was in a state to take the necessary action. Later in the same year there were more heavy snowfalls in Hampshire.

When the steeple of St Lawrence Church, Alton was struck by lightning during a violent thunderstorm on 24th June, 1880, the wardens decided to install a lightning conductor and sent for the church steeplejacks. This picture shows two of them at the top, hanging precariously onto the weather vane and posing for the camera. There are four men in the photograph and it is assumed they were roped together. Certainly they attracted a large audience.

The great snowstorm of January, 1881 brought to the Isle of Wight the worst conditions ever known. Drifting snow actually reached the rooftops in many places, villages were isolated for days and rail transport was chaotic. This picture was taken in Ventnor on the morning of 19th January. One lady who remembered the blizzard was the late Mrs Sarah Drayton of Freshwater who was 91 when her reminiscences appeared in the Isle of Wight County Press during the winter of 1963. She wrote: "The snow fell for three days and nights and it froze so hard that people were able to walk on top of hedges. I was aged nine, one of five children, and we were unable to go to school until Easter. Fortunately we had plenty of potatoes and meat as my father had a pig killed before Christmas. I managed to walk through the snow to worship at All Saints Church, Freshwater each Sunday."

Greatest snowstorm ever?

18th — 21st January, 1881

EARLY on Tuesday morning, 18th January, an icy gale-force wind raged over the south of England, followed by grains of snow which thickened fast. They were not the feathery flakes so often seen but granular, gritty and hard and they fell in wraiths, smoke-like, whipped into a frenzy. The snow penetrated chinks not known to exist. Huge drifts formed everywhere but such was the power of the wind that, in places, it swept bare one side of a street while the other was buried to roof level.

This was a storm without equal both on land and at sea. As the *Hampshire Chronicle* wrote: "No such block of human business, no such closing up of the ways of the English world has befallen us in living memory."

The accumulation of snow in the streets of Portsmouth and Gosport led to the almost total suspension of business, the borough engineer calculating that nearly 11 million cubic yards of snow had fallen on the town. Rail transport was abandoned and some citizens, travelling from Winchester to Portsmouth struggled up to their waists in snow, having left their immobilised train.

It was the same in the north of the county. At Basingstoke, the market-day streets were almost deserted. A train ran into huge drifts at Whitchurch and the guard described the experience: "I got down with my lantern and was met by the cutting gale and my face was instantly covered with a thick crust which you could neither rub nor pull off with your hand. The wind blew me backwards and forced me to keep my chin down on my chest."

Meanwhile, on the Isle of Wight, drifting reached the roof tops and Ryde was paralysed and marooned. The railway pier was wrecked, sustaining damage from the constant pounding by the high seas and from ships being dashed against it. Queen Victoria was not amused, for Osborne House was surrounded by twelve foot drifts and she was prevented from enjoying her daily walk. The storm also thwarted the pursuits of skaters who had been flocking to ice-covered waters, such as Baffin's pond in Portsmouth.

There were greater battles than that of inconvenience to skaters. The *Hampshire Telegraph* told of a postmaster, Mr Lockyer and a travelling companion, Mr Allen, who tried to reach Emsworth from Cosham. A mile beyond Drayton the storm reached such dimensions, with the snow falling in blinding sheets, that Mr Allen was forced to give up. The postmaster bravely returned to obtain some brandy, ploughed laboriously back and managed to resuscitate his colleague. They walked backwards, each spreading his jacket to protect their pony from the biting wind.

Almost frozen to death they reached Bedhampton and sank into a drift. Three labourers helped to dig out the pony chaise, whereupon the intrepid travellers continued to Emsworth.

A train at Bridgemary, near Gosport was less fortunate. Totally overwhelmed by snow it was almost completely buried and it was not until the following Monday that it was extricated.

For a while the weather relaxed its icy grip and, on Wednesday, people emerged from their half buried homes and began the slow task of digging themselves back to some sort of normality. A massive snow-clearing operation was started all over the county and at Southampton more than 11,000 cartloads were dumped into the sea.

Nature was not going to relax her stranglehold so easily. The first snow-laden depression had passed along the Channel; now another appeared and the gangs of workmen gazed at the ominous sky. Hardly had the first flakes fallen than the landscape was enveloped in a maelstrom of choking fine grained snow which made it impossible to tell sky from ground — a complete white-out, making travelling out of the question.

This storm did not affect all of the county. It swept over the southern land bordering the coast, but that included the Isle of Wight where, at St Lawrence, a further 22 inches was added to the previous fall. In some places the snow was a level three feet deep but the wind had created huge mountains, simply burying many houses. In Portsmouth, the fall of snow was so great that St Mark's Sunday School, North End collapsed under its weight.

The loss of life from exposure, hypothermia and weather-related accidents across England and Wales was around 100. In Southampton the parish of St James witnessed scenes typical of many places in southern England, with 8,000 people requiring food and fuel. Soup kitchens were set up at Northam and the Mayor established a fund for charitable relief. In London, the Thames was filled with blocks of floating ice and about 100 barges were sunk along the river. There was even a report of a 10-foot snowdrift in Oxford Street.

Vast numbers of birds died due to their food being buried. At Shanklin, on the Isle of Wight, larks were seen hopping around on the snow, looking for scraps. Presently some rooks swooped down on the larks, tore them to pieces and ate them.

The temperature plunged to 9F (-12C) on the coast where the sea was frozen, including the Inner Dock at Southampton but, inland, the temperature fell to values as low as zero farenheit. The snowstorm of

The white-out was more akin to Spitzbergen than the fair Isle of Wight. Above and below — the scene in Ryde.

January, 1881, arguably the greatest in modern history, has now passed into weather folklore. At the time it held the distinction of being a blizzard of North American proportions, with needle-like snow crystals, temperatures well below freezing and an accompanying wind that felled trees, unroofed buildings and sculptured drifts into the most extraordinary shapes. One of the most awe-inspiring sights was the great clouds of snow, swept from the cliffs around Chale and Blackgang on the southern tip of the Isle of Wight, in foglike shrouds billowing over the sea. They blotted out every discernible detail, a white-out more akin to Spitzbergen or Baffin Island than the balmy air with which this island is normally associated.

Another rare picture of the great snowstorm, when wonder and bewilderment were captured in every amazing scene. This is Rayner's Hotel, Ventnor.
Right: The bleak scene in Cowes.

Newport, showing the depth of snow outside the Guildhall.

Two horsemen set off from Mill Hill Road, Cowes to see who needed help.

Mirth and mayhem in a winter storm

December, 1886

IN late December, 1886, heavy snow again crippled Hampshire but for some it was fun. Soldiers stationed at Aldershot built a huge snow fort and, in a mock battle, it was attacked by troops under the command of Colonel Thompson. An exciting conflict ensued. The defenders offered a most determined resistance "but the fort was captured after half an hour's hard fighting". The battle was witnessed by a large crowd of spectators.

On the coast the snow was preceded by heavy rain which lashed down so heavily and noisily that the pastor of the Free Church in Clifford Street, Southampton was not able to continue with his service. Winds reached hurricane force and telegraph lines came down at Havant.

At Portswood, large trees fell and, at Woolston, women had to be carried across the road to the station. At Millers Pond, a husband had to pass his wife and children out of the window shortly before the wind wrecked his cottage. In the New Forest, people were marooned in their homes. Portsmouth escaped the ravages of the snow-storm but virtually all telegraphic communication was suspended. The lines between Fareham and Havant suffered severely "being laid low for miles".

There was serious damage on the Isle of Wight. The tunnel connecting Ryde Pier with St John's Road Station was inundated with three feet of water and the line between Smallbrook and St John's was washed away. The railway between Sandown and Newport was under water and, at Ventnor, the side of a house was blown down. At Lymington, "the wind blew a regular hurricane all night" and at Hurn Mills, near Christchurch, cattle were drowned and people had to be rescued from upstairs windows. Bournemouth lost trees in the pleasure ground, walls collapsed and telegraph lines were down.

The Waterloo end of Lymington presented a pitiful picture. Large areas of the town were submerged and drowned donkeys, pigs and fowl were seen floating about. The flood was attributed to land water from the New Forest and it was reported that such an inundation as this one had not been known before; the nearest being the tidal flood of New Year's Day, 1877.

Storm-driven seas batter the pier at Boscombe some years after its opening ceremony in 1889. Unlike many of its contemporaries, however, this pier was to prove a great survivor — resisting everything that nature could throw at it; in fact the only breach was made as a military precaution in 1940. This photograph was taken on 10th October, 1907.

Buried in snow for four days

March, 1891

AFTER the coldest December of the century, in which severe frosts and chill east winds took a high toll of the county's birdlife, the New Year of 1891 was much milder. By February, spring flowers bloomed, farmers were ahead with their sowing and, on the 28th, the thermometer stood at 66F (19C) in Southampton. Winter was over.

Or was it? As cold northerly winds sent the temperatures plummeting on 9th March, the stage was set for a most unusual combination of the elements. A vicious area of low pressure moved east along the Channel. First, rain fell, then it was mixed with snowflakes which increased in size and intensity as the temperature dropped and the easterly winds strengthened. Soon a gale of storm force screamed across Hampshire and the Isle of Wight.

At Alresford, roads became quite impassable with drifts 10 feet deep. The snow closed all roads at Fordingbridge and the mail coaches were brought in across the fields. At East and West Dean many men were employed to dig out sheep and lambs buried under huge drifts — thick wool helping them to survive in their caves of snow.

A train became entombed in the snow at Merstone Cutting on the Isle of Wight. Passengers spent the night at the nearby station and two locomotives were sent to relieve the train. They, too, became engulfed and the Railway Company manager and his men had to work all night to free the line. Further afield the Zulu Express left Paddington at 3pm on Monday 9th March and did not arrive in Plymouth until 8.30pm on the Friday, having been buried in snow on the southern flanks of Dartmoor with its 40 passengers for four days!

The snow was so deep at Owslebury that many inhabitants were unable to leave their homes for days. At Winnall, near Winchester, the drifted snow became so compressed that it blocked the main flow of the River Itchen. Fast accumulating waters had to be released over the meadows while a channel was cut.

The full fury of the storm swept the coast unhindered and the shore was littered with wreckage from Kent to Cornwall. More than 50 boats were sunk off Devon and Cornwall along with great loss of life. The landing stage at Shanklin Pier was washed several hundred yards from the structure and the night steamer carrying the mails could not depart from Ryde "owing to the atmosphere being so thick with swirling snow".

A wheat fagger at work near Alton in the summer of 1893, which was remarkable for a spring drought, and a dry and warm summer. These conditions were also ideal for the hops, and while the wheat fagger toiled on his own, whole families went into the hop gardens — from babies in prams to the old folk who wouldn't have missed the hop season for anything. The Hampshire hops were always picked during the school summer holidays and the pickers were mostly women and children. During this period the vines were grown on poles which had to be uprooted for picking. Certainly 1893 was a vintage year for both the pickers and the brewers.

It is possible that this very old photograph of a cornfield near Alton was also taken in the summer of 1893. The couple lying in the hay, Mr and Mrs Adams, were the parents of Fanny, the girl who had been cruelly hacked to death 26 years earlier in 1867. (see page 15).

There were crowds of people on shore to watch the lifeboats in action.

Storm rescue, 31st January, 1892

THERE was thick fog, stormy weather and a turbulent sea on the night of Sunday 31st January, 1892 as the four-masted steamer, *Eider* of Bremen inched her way up the Channel looking for vital signals from The Needles lighthouse. No beams on this wild night could possibly penetrate the fog and the distressed ship ran aground on the infamous Atherfield Ledge. She twisted round four or five times before settling on a cradle of rocks.

Signal rockets were fired and at 11 pm the Atherfield Lifeboat went out and brought ashore telegrams from the *Eider*'s captain asking for tugs. Meanwhile, the lifeboats from Brighstone Grange and Brook had arrived on the scene to be told by the captain that all passengers must be taken off the ship. During the day the lifeboats made 18 trips, bringing ashore 233 persons, "specie and mails." The next day, in the course of 11 journeys the lifeboats landed a further 146 people and on the days following they brought ashore more specie, bars of silver, the ship's plate and all the passengers' luggage — a total altogether of 41 journeys, £300,000 worth of specie, 500 sacks of mail and 379 grateful people. The captain and some of the crew remained on the *Eider*, but it was two months later before she was towed off the rocks. It was an amazing effort by the lifeboats and one particularly appreciated by Queen Victoria and the Emperor of Germany who presented each of the three Coxswains with a gold watch.

1800—1900 (from page 18)

1890: A great frost gripped Hampshire from late November, through December into January. December was one of the coldest of the last 200 years. In September a whirlwind sprang up at Hayling Island and there were severe gales at Portsmouth in early November.

1891: The memorable blizzard of March was followed by a cold spring and cool, cloudy summer. Harestock, near Winchester, had a penetrating frost on 12th January with 15F (-10C). On 20th August a summer storm at Portsmouth produced 1.52 inches (39 mm) of rain.

1892: Yet another cold winter at the start of the year. Colonel H.S. Knight of The Observatory, Harestock, Winchester, recorded 17F (-9.5C) on 10th January and a similar figure on 17th February. A heatwave in April saw the temperature soar to 74F (23C) at Southampton as early as 6th April.

1893:. At Liss there was an absolute drought of 61 days from 4th March to 15th May. This was followed by a dry and rather warm summer, although a downpour at Portsmouth on 18th August produced 1.11 inches (28 mm) of rain. The temperature of 93.4F (34C) at Osborne, Isle of Wight, on 19th June, made it the hottest place in the British Isles that day. Southampton on the same day basked in 91F (33C).

Throughout history there had been no celebration to match the Diamond Jubilee of Queen Victoria, which took place on 22nd June, 1897 in brilliant sunshine. The Queen had spent many of her recent years at Osborne House, near Cowes but on this occasion she left Buckingham Palace for a procession in an open carriage through the cities of London and Westminster and on to the working class area of Southwark.

Celebrations were held in every hamlet, village, town and city in the country and, at Winchester (above), thousands lined the streets, which were bedecked in Union Jacks.

The celebrations in Portsmouth attracted hundreds of thousands of people, especially to see the firework display on Southsea Common. The Portsmouth News wrote: "The crush which ensued on the conclusion of the display when the multitudes turned for home, the rush for vehicles, the desperate fight for seats in tram cars, the squeezing by the Pier Hotel, the thousands of great feet that trod upon dresses and corns and kicked ankles and shins, the struggle to get drinks — all this can only properly be conceived by anybody who got half killed in the crowd. The presence of perambulators with crying babies, the desperate struggle of numerous bicyclists mixed up with the crowd and the shouts of excited, in some instances, reckless drivers, all added to the confusion".

During Victoria's reign, Britain had seen the advent of steam trains and steam ships, the coming of electricity, the bicycle, the telephone, the telegram and the post office. The British empire had become the largest and richest the world had ever witnessed and Hampshire, like the rest of Britain, wanted to celebrate.

Food for the hungry children

1800 — 1900 (continued)

1894: In January outside Winchester 12F (-11C) was recorded on 5th. In Portsmouth, it was as low as 14F (-10C). March had some cheerful sunshine and a heatwave occurred in April but generally the summer was cool.

1895: A notably cold January was followed by a bitter February; one of the coldest ever known. Southampton Water became frozen over by the end of February and Portsmouth Harbour iced up. Barges were welded in the ice for weeks near Hayling and there was skating off Thorney.

At Harestock Observatory, Winchester, the temperature on 7th February fell as low as 5F (-15C). At Farnborough, benevolent workers helped to feed 200 poor and hungry children in the town when the severe weather set in. A cart laden with bread and groceries toured the district in late February, handing out provisions to the needy. Many folk contributed to the funds of the Aldershot soup kitchen and the committee was able to distribute some 400 quarts of soup each day and offer a free breakfast to 800 children in Aldershot. At the barracks very little activity took place due to the bone-chilling frost. The *Military Gazette* reported that the cavalry were "simply confining their attention to exercising on straw tracks laid down in front of the barracks". Cattle and men were killed by lightning in the Portsmouth area during a thunderstorm in August. In November 1.78 inches (45mm) of rain fell outside the Portsmouth Health Department's offices in just 24 hours, the heaviest daily total of the decade. More gales lashed the county mid-month.

1896: An eclipse of the moon was observed at the end of February. In December, rumblings from an earthquake were felt at Southsea.

1897: After a frosty January, floods caused chaos at Fareham in February. A great storm occurred on Wednesday 3rd March, causing devastation along the south coast and in The Solent. July and early August were warm and sunny. Corn could be reaped at Havant on 17th July.

1898: A snowstorm on 21st February was said to be the heaviest since 1881 in the Bournemouth area, with an average depth of nine inches.

After a cool summer, the mercury reached its greatest values in September and there were 16 days above 70F (21C) with temperatures in the mid eighties quite widespread on the 6th.

1899: A dry year. An 'annus mirabilis' in terms of weather, but it was bad for all forms of crops except wheat. Springs were low, an observer at Winchfield noted and most ponds dry.

During the summer a mirage of the Isle of Wight was reflected into the atmosphere and was "a wondrous sight at Hayling".

A figure stands on the ice which lay thickly across the Basingstoke Canal at Odiham during the bitterly cold winter of 1895. It was in February of this year that Portsmouth Harbour iced up.

They threaded the Needles on a day in June

Alfred Tennyson, poet laureate since 1850 and a great personal friend of Queen Victoria, was a frequent visitor to the Isle of Wight, eventually moving to a house at Bonchurch. In 1853 he stayed for a while with his literary friends James White and Edmund Peel, also residents of the "fair isle". One summer day, the three of them took a boat around the Needles and

Tennyson later wrote:

Two poets and a mighty dramatist
Threaded the Needles on a day in June.
Upon the Ocean hung a lucid mist,
And round the cliffs the seabirds'

plaintive tune
Resounded as they row'd beneath the sun

*The terrible floods, after the storm in July 1899, killed one of these tram horses at Southsea.
The incident occurred at the flood point in Clarendon Road, opposite the recreation ground
near The Circle. It regularly flooded during storms but on this occasion the water was abnor-
mally deep. The tram operated on the Beach - Mansions route.*

A Sunday in summertime

23rd July, 1899

THE smell of the traditional Sunday roast still lingered in hundreds of Portsmouth homes as families
prepared to relax on this Sabbath afternoon. Moments later many of those houses were uninhabit-
able. Shortly after 2 pm a storm of amazing severity
broke over the city. Vivid lightning darted from
angry clouds, rain fell in deafening torrents and in
minutes the streets of Portsmouth were filled with
filthy water which surged into homes.

An account in the *Hampshire Telegraph* recalled
how "the lightning flashed and the thunder roared,
terrifying the timid and arresting the unwanted
attention of even the stout hearted". Properties in
Chapel, Fratton and Southsea were struck by lightning. Mr and Mrs Talbot and family were sitting at
dinner when lightning struck the ceiling, darting
along nails and sending an eight-foot slab of
plasterwork crashing onto their table in Southsea.

The tower of the chapel in Portsea Cemetery was
hit and stonework crashed through the vestry roof.
Muddy-coloured floodwater, contaminated with sewage, rushed into all low-lying roads. The Edinburgh
Road Congregational Chapel had two feet of water "so
that it was impossible to hold divine service in the
evening."

One boy swam from the Telegraph office to the
church and another swam on his back in Greetham
Street. The railway line between Portsmouth and
Fratton was buried under two feet of water. A tram
horse died after getting stuck in floodwater which
reached his shoulders. A pony at Brandon Road,
East Southsea was led to safety by a Royal Navy
bluejacket but in the process the unfortunate man
tripped and was submerged in the floodwater. He
recovered to lead a sow to safety by its ear but the pig
panicked and tore off the man's trousers.

This incredible rainfall amounted to 3.25 inches at
Milton and it was estimated that 347 million gallons
fell in the district — 50 times the amount used by
Portsmouth people on an average day.

Chapter Three: 1900 — 1910

Damp and stormy decade

1900: A very wet February with 6.3 inches (158mm) of rain on melted snow at Sandown, Isle of Wight. A blizzard on 13th-14th February drifted to a great depth and all traffic was halted at West Dean. It was followed by heavy rain which continued with barely any intermission to the end of the month, making work on the farms well nigh impossible. However, a heatwave in July sent the temperature as high as 92.5F (33C) at Hartley Wintney on the 19th.

1901: A severe spell of cold from 3rd January to the 9th. Four inches of snow fell and the mercury plummeted to 3F (-16C). Even household items indoors froze up at West Dean and there was considerable damage to plants. On 9th January the temperature fell at Swarraton to -2F (-19C), one of the coldest readings ever known in Hants.

1902: Hampshire had its coldest February of the Edwardian years. At Selborne on 29th July, hail the size of marrowfat peas fell so heavily that lawns turned white. Storm after storm occurred until 10th August. It was a terrible time for the holidaymakers and also for the late breeding birds. Day by day during this cold and wet summer, the swifts, swallows and housemartins gradually disappeared.

1903: A wet year with October producing 10.43 inches (260mm) of rain at Bishop's Waltham. Flooding caused much disruption in parts of Hampshire. Shopfronts in Winchester were damaged by a violent thunderstorm and heavy rain in mid June.

1904: There was an unusual thunderstorm in January but, by all accounts from across the county, it was a genial year which resulted in a record fruit crop "especially strawberries which were so abundant much was left on the ground to rot".

1905: Atmospheric pressure reached 31 inches on the Isle of Wight on 29th January. A dry July with less than a third of an inch of rain at Milford on Sea. October was very cold with nine nights of frost in a row from 17th to 25th. On the night of 25th, Southampton shivered at just 21F (-6C). At Totland Bay on the Isle of Wight, a brilliant display of the aurora borealis was seen on 15th November with the northern sky a vivid rose colour.

1906: Grayshott was on the edge of a devastating evening thunderstorm which struck Guildford, Surrey on 2nd August. In just 20 minutes, 1.17 inches (30mm) of rain poured down. September began with an exceptional heatwave, temperatures not falling below 67F (19C) at Totland Bay on 2nd. During the day, the mercury had soared to 82F (28C) at Southampton and the city had bathed in more than 12 hours of sunshine. The year ended with snow which fell thickly during the evening of Christmas Day and lay several inches deep by morning.

1907: Hail and lightning at Southampton on 2nd January, while on 24th a temperature of 18F (-8C) was recorded at Fordingbridge and a bitterly cold easterly wind added to the chill during the day. At Ryde, Isle of Wight, the sea was frozen for about 20 yards. Next day, the snow at Bournemouth measured one and a half inches, the heaviest fall for six years. At Sandown, skating was enjoyed on 26th January. March was a glorious month. At Kempsey, Bournemouth, the last two weeks had a "remarkable spell of beautiful and rainless weather with brilliant sunshine and cloudless skies". The summer was dry and cold at Bournemouth but Fordingbridge gathered 9.12 inches of rain in October, a monthly figure exceeded only twice in the preceding 33 years.

1908: The year went down in history books for its famous snowstorm on 25th April. Snow depths included 22 inches at Oakley, 18 inches at West Dean, 15 inches at Alton, 14 inches at Freshwater and 10 inches at Cowes. Another snowstorm late in the year brought seven inches of fine powdery snow to Southampton on 29th December. Liphook reported -1F (-18C). This was the coldest temperature recorded in Great Britain during the whole of 1908.

1909: A sunny March with more than 350 hours of sunshine at Totland. This averaged a remarkable 11.3 hours a day. October was the wettest on record at Petersfield and it rained every day at Hartley Wintney. On the Isle of Wight, Wootton recorded 4.43 inches (113mm) between 26th and 28th October.

Winchester in a stormy spell during June, 1902.

Another precious piece of Britain falls into the sea. Picture shows the damage done to the sea wall, east of Ryde by the high tides of 1905.

Living with fear of extinction

ON the Isle of Wight, which is entirely exposed to the fury of the Atlantic, many villages have disappeared into the waves and, for centuries, communities have lived with the fear of extinction. In the western extremity, Freshwater Bay has been entirely hollowed out by the sea which has taken the village of Easton. The old village of St Helens which once stood between Ryde and Brading Haven has also gone. So has the original Brading Harbour, which was overrun by the sea despite an attempt in the reign of James 1 to reclaim it.

An article in the *Isle of Wight County Press* as long ago as 1905, tells of the fate which was befalling those living near the road to Ventnor. "The cliffs are continually falling", says the writer. "I have been shown a row of houses, known as Devonshire Terrace which was some years since pulled down and rebuilt at a greater distance from the sea; and there is now a house close to the cliff and permanently untenanted because of the fear that it will collapse. The path giving access to Bonchurch has continually to be shifted, yet an aged inhabitant recalls the time when he could not, with all his strength, throw a stone from the present pathway to the sea."

The famous Undercliff is a tract of shore formed by fallen cliffs which were described in 1905 as "a picturesque ruin". Over the centuries hundreds of acres of cliff have collapsed, and enormous subsidences continue to occur. One of the most astonishing landslips was in 1799 when a farm-house and 100 acres of land were completely destroyed. An eye witness wrote at the time: "The whole of the ground from the cliff above was in motion, which motion was directed to the sea, nearly in a straight line. The ground above, immediately under St Catherine's, kept gliding down and at last rushed on with a great violence. All around here westward from the Sand Rock is a scene of bleakness and desolation, testimony to the fury of the winter storms."

Further west, the famous Needles remain as a striking, solitary fragment of land which has been wrenched away from its parent earth. There are five rocks, although only three rise sheer and bold out of the water. The last was isolated early in the nineteenth century before which the connecting portion was perforated to form a large arch. A rock much higher than any now existing which formed a slender pinnacle of about 120 feet, fell in the year 1764. This was the original needle and was called by seamen as "the pillar of Lot's wife". In later maps it was known as "The Ghost".

Warm and healthy — Old Ventnor where the climate was "unsurpassed anywhere in the world".

But it was also the boom years

THE early years of the 20th century were boom years for coastal resorts in Hampshire and, particularly the Isle of Wight which had been so popularised by the late Queen. In southern England tourism was now the most flourishing industry and every town competed for a share of the "sunshine market".

Writers, eager to promote the Isle of Wight, were enthusiastic about the weather and described how the big test of climate was its general effect on vegetation and how the island was two or three weeks ahead of mainland England.

Others admitted that there was snow, sometimes, and rain pretty often. Hope Moncrieff, in 1908, wrote: "The north and east sides are, of course, more exposed to bracing winds and the resorts from Cowes to Sandown come into favour in the summer season which fills the sails of yachts and pleasure boats. The 'back of the island' is more stormed upon by the Atlantic gales while one half of it, the famous Undercliff, is so snugly shut in to the north as to make a winter garden of myrtles, fuchsias and arbutus."

Here it was that a Miss Malaprop complained of this island as 'not embracing enough' and suggested the Isle of Man might be a better place.

Ventnor's reputation as a health resort was, in the early 1900s, gaining momentum. In his book *The Climate of the Undercliff*, John Whitehouse said of Ventnor. "The air is almost, if not wholly, the pure air of the sea. No land breezes can be felt; no streams or ponds of fresh water exist of any considerable size. The geographical situation, the southern exposure and the tremendous 'Downs' have given to Ventnor a climate which cannot be found elsewhere and which I believe is unsurpassed in the world for the treatment of pulmonary diseases."

Man who saved Winchester Cathedral

WINCHESTER Cathedral, built by the Normans, has experienced whirlwinds and tornadoes, great storms and gales of hurricane force. Thunder has boomed around her, lightning has crackled and fireballs have run down the richly ornate towers. She has withstood all — except floods.

The city is situated on the flood plain of the Itchen and in 1905 an architect, making a routine report on the condition of the building, discovered the Cathedral was not immune to the waters which so frequently lapped the ancient streets. He suggested there might be one or two defects.

Investigations showed that the entire building site was flooded with water that ebbed and flowed with the seasons and the cathedral was sinking on its rotting timber foundations. So it was resolved to excavate and pull out the age-old timbers and replace them with good solid concrete and masonry. The work facing the experts was unique and their ultimate solution of the difficulty was also unique.

They employed a professional diver who could work under water.

The diver employed was William Walker who was kept busy laying bags of water-setting concrete on the chalk and filling in with loose concrete until everything was sealed. With him was an army of workmen who took almost seven years to complete the job. Walker, however, was the hero. He worked alone under the Cathedral, underpinning, repairing and strengthening. Wearing his diver's outfit he handled an estimated 25,800 bags of concrete, 114,900 concrete blocks, 900,000 bricks. He became known as "the man who saved Winchester Cathedral" and is buried within. The whole work cost in excess of £12,000.

Throughout the 20th century, the River Itchen has continued to cause problems, particularly in days of great floods, and many more thousands of pounds have been spent repairing, improving and altering the great Cathedral.

Winchester Cathedral wasn't the only church which suffered from the effects of the weather. On 14th January, 1904, after a day of localised thunderstorms and heavy rain, Godshill Church on the Isle of Wight was struck by lightning. Half of the square tower was demolished and masonry was sent crashing down into the church causing hundreds of pounds worth of damage. Visitors to this beautiful small village were saddened to see the ivy-covered tower in such a state.

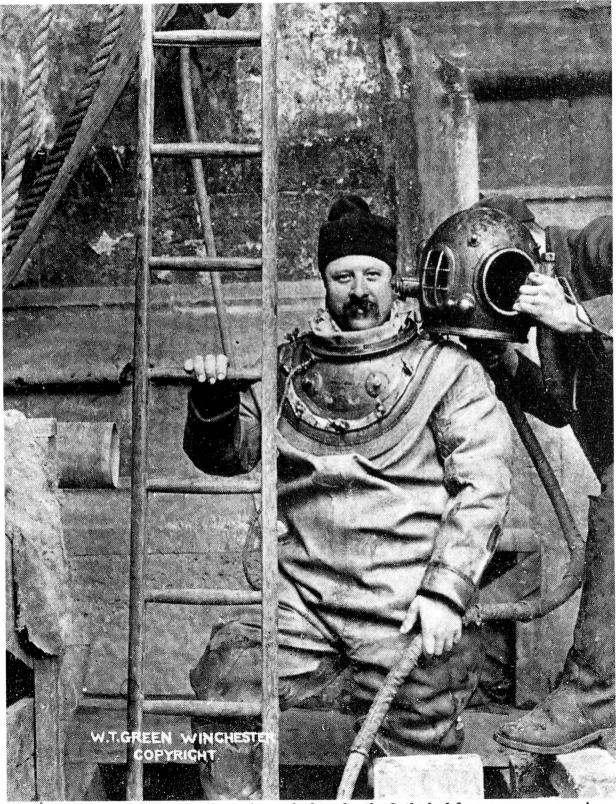

W.T.GREEN WINCHESTER
COPYRIGHT

Historic picture of William Walker, who worked under the Cathedral for seven years, wearing his diver's outfit.

Watching the sports at Seaview, Isle of Wight on 30th August, 1906 — a day which enjoyed a temperature of 82F (28C).

The best Edwardian summer

August-September, 1906

THE great heatwave of late August-early September, 1906 saw temperatures reach the nineties in parts of Hampshire which put the tinder dry countryside under enormous fire risk. While firemen were busy with blazes which swept through woods, consumed haystacks and demolished timber buildings, holidaymakers, cricketers and carnival organisers were enjoying this late burst of sunshine. The picture shows a sports day at Ryde which took place a few days before the revival of the Ryde Regatta which was an oustanding success. "Those interested in the prosperity of Ryde are all rejoicing", said the *Isle of Wight County Press.*

Meanwhile at Sandown, there was trouble on the beaches. The local council had reduced the number of licences normally granted for bathing machines on the esplanade and there were many hot tempers to match the rise in temperature. On the day when the thermometer reached 91F (32C), in the north of Hampshire, a public meeting was held into the question — to bathe, or not to bathe? Protestors said that insufficient bathing machines were turning people away; many were moving on to other resorts for their holidays. The council got the message. At the end of the season they debated the problem again and awarded 177 new licenses for the 1907 season.

On the mainland, visitors to Southampton enjoyed several days when the sun shone for more than 12 hours and temperatures were in the mid-eighties. A south-easterly breeze saved the south coast from the great heat which affected Alton, Aldershot and Fleet.

The weather on Tuesday 4th September enabled workhouse inmates at Romsey to enjoy an outing to Redbridge and Nursling in three-horse carriages. Extra tobacco was handed out to the men and sweets and biscuits to the others and "their best summer raiment was donned for the occasion".

In the remainder of the Edwardian years there was no repeat of the heatwave of September, 1906. Cold weather prevailed in 1907 and, at Christchurch, the weather observer, Jane Lassell said the hottest weather was the 70F (21C) reached in May.

The wreck of the Ryde lifeboat in January, 1907

Ryde lifeboat tragedy

THE wind was West-South-West and increasing in force as the Ryde Lifeboat, *Selina* was launched on 1st January, 1907 to rescue the master of a barge *Jane* who was adrift on a small boat. Despite a long search they failed to find the man and, when nearing the pier on the return journey, a heavy squall capsized the lifeboat.

A policeman on shore heard cries for help coming from the sea and alerted the coastguards who saw the *Selina* drifting, bottom up, eastward of Southsea Castle. The crew of seven were clinging to the keel.

Two of the men, second coxswain Henry Howard and Frank Hayes succumbed to exposure and slipped into the sea. Their colleagues attempted to hold them up but the waves washed the men away.

The disaster occurred as mild air battled into Hampshire after the white Christmas, days earlier.

Portsmouth Station during the floods of 6th October, 1907

A famous Spring snowstorm

25th April, 1908

THIS was a snowstorm to rival the greatest that any January could offer. It raged for more than 18 hours and completely buried spring flowers. It brought down trees and telegraph poles. It ruined crops, damaged telephone wires, caused loss of life and caught the people of Hampshire and the Isle of Wight totally by surprise.

After the blizzards of January, 1908, spring had burst upon southern England, bringing warmth and a welcome freshness. Shakespeare wrote of the "uncertain glories of an April day" and, as if to prove him right, Friday 24th began with sunshine and showers, and ended with unseasonably cold weather as night-time neared. A low pressure area had become embedded in a cold northerly airstream over Hampshire.

Snow began to fall at 4 am on Saturday morning and continued without intermission for 18 hours. By midday, roads were already impassable, the depth of snow was two feet and it was piling higher by the minute. During the afternoon, a high blustering wind blew it into massive drifts and such was the force of the driving, blinding snow that it was impossible to walk.

Memories of January, 1881 were brought sharply into focus as the Hampshire countryside slowly disappeared under its white mantle. The *Portsmouth Evening News* described the ferocity of the snowstorm "of a like which had not been seen for years. Hampshire is at a standstill", they said. "It is impossible to reach the villages and people will have to go short of their weekly provisions. The mail is suspended and the annual fair day at Alton postponed. There are a few sleighs in use — an extraordinary sight for the end of April. Many lambs have died and the storm has destroyed all prospects of a good fruit harvest which previously existed."

The snowstorm in Southampton was terrific. On Saturday morning with the blizzard still approaching its zenith, gangs of men were busy digging out the city's trams, while the fire brigade assisted in clearing the roads. The *Evening News* said: "Trade is suspended and so are the trains, owing to the lines being covered to a depth of many inches. The telegraph running from the dock to Waterloo has broken down but the Post Office line has fortunately escaped damage. Such a visitation has not been experienced in Southampton for 27 years."

At Winchester, the aviary in the Abbey grounds was completely wrecked. The *Hampshire Independent* wrote: "The extensive, small-meshed wire caught and held the snow, which became such a tremendous weight that the stout iron uprights and cross-bars yielded and the whole fell with a great noise. Fortunately the birds escaped unhurt and only a couple of doves were killed but it was curious to see the goldfinches gathered at one end of the aviary in fright of the iron wreckage".

Many extra men and horses were employed in Winchester to clear the snow and shoot it into the river at Beck Street. The *Hampshire Independent* said that such a snowstorm within a week of May Day "cannot be recalled by the oldest inhabitant" and at Bournemouth it was described as the heaviest blizzard ever experienced. All steamboat traffic was abandoned and promenade Spring concerts on the pier were suspended.

The Isle of Wight suffered similar disruptions but quickly lived up to its reputation as the "sunny isle". Sunday was warm with blue skies and within a few hours the snow was melting. By Monday there was little evidence of the infamous Spring snowstorm.

Spring, 1908 at Ryde — and no sign of the holidaymakers!

High Street, Lymington on 25th April, 1908.

Clearing the footpaths at Alresford on the same day.

A Christmas card scene in Andover — in April, 1908.

Slow progress for this horse and cart in High Street, Lyndhurst on 25th April, 1908.

Springtime in Southampton at the tram junction on 25th April, 1908.

The scene in Basingstoke on 25th April, 1908.

This was the desolate scene in Worthy Road, Winchester on 25th April, 1908, as the great snowstorm closed in on a world of daffodils, cuckoos and bright spring sunshine. Across Hampshire it snowed without intermission for 18 hours and such was the force of the driving, blinding blizzard that it was impossible to walk. In Winchester, as in other areas, the snow disappeared almost as quickly as it came.

The penetrating bow of the liner, St Paul had embedded itself amidships into the Gladiator. 34 seamen lost their lives.

Tragedy in the April blizzard

25th April, 1908

THE great blinding blizzard of 25th April, 1908 was responsible for a terrible tragedy at sea, when an American liner, the *St Paul*, leaving Southampton on her voyage to New York collided with a British cruiser, the *Gladiator*, in the entrance to The Solent. Although the accident happened near the shore, 34 seamen, all from the cruiser, lost their lives.

Passengers on the *St Paul* told reporters how they heard an enormous crash and saw that the penetrating bow of the liner had embedded itself amidships into the *Gladiator*. The engines of the liner were immediately reversed and the boats lowered. The *St Paul*, on freeing herself, glided slowly backwards but the *Gladiator* simultaneously caught the full force of the blizzard broadside on and heeled over, hurling sailors into the water. Others jumped overboard and many were immediately picked up.

The commanding officer of the *Gladiator* ordered full steam to be made for the beach. The foundering vessel, badly holed and filling with water, was able to get fairly close to the shore and the survivors were picked up by rescue parties.

The Sussex Daily News in the issue of Monday 27th April said a strange spectacle met journalists on the Sunday as they crossed to Ryde and sped by motor car across the snow-clad island to Yarmouth Bay. "Straight ahead, amid the now-placid waters of the Solent, which danced and sparkled in the sunlight lay on its side the hull of the *Gladiator* like some huge derelict whale. Masts and funnels were submerged but the port side was exposed to view. The wreck was less than 150 yards from the beach on a sandy ledge. All about her were pleasure boats filled with sailors engaged in rescue work. Along the shore sauntered the surviving members of the crew dressed in the motley garb that only a shipwrecked mariner can devise while nearby lay at anchor the battleship *Prince George* which had come down from Spithead to supervise the salvage operation."

One survivor told the newspaper how they had left Portland for a straighforward journey to Portsmouth. "The weather was fine with some snow falling until we reached The Needles when a blinding blizzard enveloped us, forming a thick curtain through which it was impossible to peer more than 200 yards. The look-out men in the bows and the signal man at the siren had orders to blow five-second blasts to warn shipping of our approach. We eased down and began to feel our way up the Solent. There was a huge crash and I saw the liner wedged into our vessel."

There was no panic on board but many men were killed, or badly injured by the ripping open of the plates and ironwork as the collision occurred. Others died as they were thrown into the sea.

The *St Paul*, carrying 600 passengers, returned to Southampton.

Sam Cody, with an Indian friend at Farnborough. The weather conditions were unfavourable on the day of his first great flight.

Sam Cody — the first man to fly

16th May, 1908

THE Hampshire weather played a key role in the extraordinary life of Colonel Samuel Cody, the pioneer aviator who experimented with man-lifting kites at the Balloon School, Aldershot and then obtained permission from the War Office to build a flying machine, using the engine from a dismantled airship.

Cody, a naturalised Briton who was born in Texas, built his machine with the help of family and friends and then waited for many days for suitable weather. On 16th May, 1908 there was little or no wind but Cody had become impatient. Despite the unfavour-

able weather conditions he picketed his "aeroplane" to a tree at Farnborough, started the engine, built up the thrust to full power and then signalled to friends to release the ropes.

The machine rose, moved forward with gradually increasing speed for about 200 yards, then landed, ran some distance and came to rest. Colonel Cody, then aged 47, had made the first recorded flight in Great Britain.

Colonel Cody continued to make great progress in the next few years but tragically, in 1913, he died in an air crash.

Only the year, 1908, is given as the date for this photograph, but it could well have been an August outing to Downton, near Milford on Sea, for the Ringwood postal officials on a day when the weather was unseasonably cold. Although the gentlemen have found a sheltered spot for their picnic, they still find it necessary to keep their coats on.

A few months later there was more snow for the beleaguered county of Hampshire.
Boscombe in December, 1908.

Moustaches were frosted an icy white

THE year 1908 was famous for two snowstorms. On 29th December, deep powdery snow buried Hampshire again under a white blanket more than seven inches deep during the lowest temperatures the county had experienced for many years.

The cold air was dragged in by a depression which swung down across the country from the north west. Liphook shivered with a numbing -2F (-19C), a degree of cold rarely known in southern Britain.

A correspondent on the *Evening News* at Portsmouth described a walk in the snowbound city:

"Things had a queer look, when you could see them at all through the blinding frozen snow which cut your face like whips, turned your eyebrows and moustache an icy white and frosted the "bangs" of every girl and young woman you met so that she looked like a feminine edition of Father Christmas. The city ground to a standstill. The wheels of the trams spun slowly round but could not haul the carriages. Of motors there were none, of horses few. Round every corner the violent blasts turned the whips of the powdery snow particles into scorpions."

DS AT LYMINGTON
LWAY CROSSING. B

DURING October 1909 it rained incessantly; in fact, at Portsmouth, there were only three dry days in the whole of the month and at Hartley Wintney, there were none at all. The wettest day was the 27th when 2.10 inches fell, a deluge equalled only twice in 20 years. At Portsmouth, low-lying roads turned into rivers and the tram service had to be halted for some hours. At the junction of Malvern Road and Clarendon Road the floodwater was 20 inches deep.

On the Isle of Wight, some children had to be taken to school by cart while others waded knee-deep through the floods. Farmers suffered greatly and there were considerable losses of lambs, ewes and pigs. At Yarmouth, the heavy seas drove a barge into the pier and 150 feet of the structure was badly damaged.

At the time it was Petersfield's wettest October on record and at Portsmouth, 7.39 inches of rain was measured in the first 28 days of the month. There was much flooding, as shown in the pictures of Lymington (top) and Morton Common on the Isle of Wight.

An Edwardian summer stroll on the South Parade, Southsea.

Competing for the sunshine market

THE first decade of the new century were the halcyon years for the holiday industry. Although the summers were generally poor, warm spells in 1904 and 1906 attracted thousands of people to the Hampshire and Isle of Wight resorts, where piers, promenades, hotels, theatres, amusement arcades and letting houses were being built at an incredible rate.

The photograph shows an Edwardian family walking towards the South Parade Pier at Southsea which had just been re-opened after a disastrous fire in 1904. The new pier had landing stages for pleasure steamers, a roller skating rink and a grand theatre.

Piers were first built to provide access to steam ferries and pleasure boats and the South Parade Pier provided an excellent service to the Isle of Wight. Portsmouth's first was the Victoria Pier, named in honour of the Queen's visit in 1842, the year of its reconstruction. In 1861, the Clarence Pier was

opened and the Victoria lost its popularity and its traffic. Battered by successive storms, it was finally washed away in 1925 and not rebuilt.

The Clarence with its pavilion and adjacent Esplanade Hotel was connected to Portsmouth and Southsea by tramway and was the most popular of all. In January, 1941 the pier, pavilion and hotel were destroyed by German bombs and the pier was rebuilt with a funfair in the 1960's.

A revolutionary scheme, introduced to Southsea in 1910, caused much controversy. For the first time mixed bathing in the sea was authorised; until that time bathing machines were strictly segregated and ladies bathed west of Clarence Pier while gentlemen were restricted to the east. All of them, however, benefited from the warmest sea water in England, especially in August when the Channel averages 63F (17C).

Chapter Four: 1910 — 1919

Unsettled — on all fronts

1910: On 7th May, King Edward VII died of pneumonia. Although there were one or two warm days in June, the summer was cool. Severe gales left a trail of havoc on 16th December. This was the year in which the River Seine in Paris burst its banks, flooding the city and drowning many people. There were great fears that the Louvre Gallery would be inundated with flood water and arrangements were made to move priceless treasures.

1911: A splendid summer with plenty of hot, sunny, dry weather. However, it did bring with it some problems. At Bishop's Waltham, a fearful sandstorm on 29th July covered roads and gardens in several inches of sand.
At Totland Bay on the Isle of Wight, 2,115 hours of sunshine were recorded during the year, a figure almost worthy of the Mediterranean.

1912: A remark from a farmer in Upton Grey set the mood for this year. "It was one of the worst years known since 1879 in North Hampshire and I do not know of a single farm that has done well." It was a very wet year, the summer especially was a complete contrast to 1911. At Hythe, August had four inches more than the average amount of rain and this being at harvest time, the result was a heavy loss. Wheat was only fit to feed to the pigs and the straw was in some cases 'only two feet in height instead of four feet'. There was no relief on Christmas Day, either. At Fareham "the Christmas weather was cheerless in the extreme, the rain falling in sheets practically all day".
   Two historic events are worth noting. Captain Scott reached the South Pole on 18th January, 1912. The party was overwhelmed in a blizzard on their return journey and all perished. On 15th April, the "unsinkable" White Star liner, *Titanic*, on her maiden voyage to New York, struck an iceberg in the waters of the North Atlantic, 1,500 people drowned.

1913: The summer of 1913 was very dull with a deficit of sunshine which, over the year as a whole, amounted to an average of just one hour per day.

1914: The year began with cold, dry weather but, in December ended mild and wet with 11.47 inches (293mm), nearly three times the monthly average. The mercury did reach 91F (33C) at Upper Somborne on 1st July but heavy thunderstorms gave 1.4 inches of rain at Selborne on 19th.

1915: Heavy rain in January brought floods to West Hampshire and serious inundations over the border in Salisbury. It was a wet year with December, especially, beset by one long train of depressions bringing copious rains. Bishop's Waltham was drenched with more than 10 inches (254mm). As much as 52.8 inches fell during the year at Petersfield which amounted to 40 per cent more than the average. The December rains caused flooding in Hilsea and Portsmouth.

1916: A snowy spell of weather in February and March. The worst conditions for many years on the Isle of Wight when blizzards and hurricane force winds combined to cause damage to every island town and village. Transport links, including the floating bridge and the steam launch between Fountain Pier and East Cowes, were suspended because of the conditions and roads across the island were blocked by snow and fallen trees. Scores of buildings on the island were damaged including St Thomas's Church, Newport and Duffett's brewery, Ryde.
The summer started remarkably cool and dull but 21st May was brilliantly sunny. On this day, clocks in Britain were put forward by an hour, for the first time, in a controversial plan to save daylight hours. It was decided to put them back again in October. Each of the four months from December 1916 to March 1917 was, up to that time, the coldest at Totland since 1895. There were 55 air frosts between the beginning of November and the end of March.

1917: After a prolonged cold winter which continued into April, it warmed up in May and June but this led to some heavy thundery falls of rain. On 28th June, a remarkable 4.94 inches of rain fell at West Tytherley between Winchester and Salisbury. On this day, Britain's heaviest ever daily rainfall occurred. This was at Bruton, Somerset, which collected 9.56 inches. A few weeks later in August thousands of English soldiers, fighting the third battle of Ypres, became bogged down in the Flanders mud after ceaseless rainstorms.

1918: December got off to a warm start with a balmy 60F(16C) on 1st at Sandown. In some parts of the south, it was the warmest December since 1868.

1919: A cool year with July the coldest since 1888. May was the best month with an absolute drought of 23 days at Ryde from 12th May to 3rd June.

By rowing boat to school through the streets of Portsmouth in December, 1910.

Flooding on land and drama at sea

16th December, 1910

LARGE parts of the Hampshire coast were battered by hurricane force winds on 16th December, 1910. This fierce Friday storm turned the sea into a foaming cauldron in which lifeboatmen from Hayling, Southsea and Bembridge were to risk their lives.

The Hayling lifeboat battled against towering waves to rescue seven crew members from a schooner, *Blanche*, which eventually went ashore at West Wittering. The distressed vessel was carrying 285 tons of wheat and the crew had spent two days drifting around the Channel and were in great need of food.

Lifeboatmen from Southsea endured 15 hours at sea in the most terrible conditions. Their boat frequently filled with water as giant waves tossed the craft around the tumultuous sea. For two hours they battled to reach a 2,000-ton steamer only to find the vessel had not intended to raise an alarm. The exhausted crew, with only two pounds of biscuits and a quart of whisky on board, turned the lifeboat around and headed home in the teeth of the gale. During a frightful journey which took 11 hours, two crew members saw a mountainous wave heading in their direction. They grabbed their lifeline but the force of the water was so great they lost their grip. Colleagues managed to catch them and haul them aboard but they were both injured.

On land, there were floods at Portsmouth and one in 20 homes in the city suffered structural damage. Pupils of Broad Street Council School were taken to their lessons by boat because the water was so deep. Hundreds of glass-covered wreaths at Kingston Cemetery were smashed and the pinnacle on the entrance gate was toppled by the furious winds.

The clouds are clearing as a Coronation procession moves through Havant.

Damp Coronation, then the big heat

THE year 1911 was an eventful one. Two members of an alleged anarchist gang were burned to death after being cornered by 1,000 soldiers in "The siege of Sydney Street", Winston Churchill was appointed First Lord of the Admiralty, the largest ship in the world, the White Star liner, *Titanic,* was launched, the Norwegian explorer Amundsen became the first man to reach the South Pole and King George V was crowned head of the world's greatest empire.

It was also a wonderful summer with record-breaking temperatures in August. Sadly, the great heat sent the death rate soaring, particularly in London where the mortality rate for all ages was 19 per 1,000 and it was declared the second most unhealthy city in the world. During the last week in August, 855 children died.

Throughout Hampshire and the Isle of Wight, there were joyous scenes for Coronation Day and a small interruption in this magnificent summer weather failed to spoil the festivities. In parts of the south-east more than half an inch of rain fell on the big day but the sun did manage to make an appearance at intervals.

A few weeks later, Hampshire was wilting under the hottest sun known for many years. At Micheldever, on 9th August, the temperature climbed to 94F (34C). Two houses collapsed in Lime Street, Aldershot, apparently because the rafters warped in the heat. Fortunately no-one was hurt, the occupants escaping in time. *The Times* reported that 1,000 acres of woodland were destroyed near Aldershot and troops were engaged in defeating the flames.

It was on 9th August, 1911 that Epsom and Canterbury both recorded a sweltering 98F (37C), which was to remain, until 1990, the hottest reading Britain had ever registered.

+

IN MEMORY OF

PERCY DEACON,	AGED 17 YEARS.
WILLIAM DIBDEN,	AGED 18 YEARS.
CHARLES HENRY DAVIES,	AGED 19 YEARS.
AMBROSE HOOD,	AGED 21 YEARS.
STANLEY GEORGE HICKMAN,	AGED 21 YEARS.
LEONARD MARK HICKMAN,	AGED 24 YEARS.
LEWIS HICKMAN,	AGED 32 YEARS.

ALL OF THIS PARISH, WHO WERE LOST IN THE WRECK OF THE S.S. "TITANIC", ON APRIL 15TH 1912, THROUGH COLLISION WITH AN ICEBERG, IN THE ATLANTIC.

ERECTED BY PARISHIONERS AND FRIENDS.

Among the estimated 1,500 people drowned when the Titanic went down were these seven young men from the parish of Bramshaw in the New Forest, who were looking forward to a new life in America. Their names are remembered on this memorial in the parish church.

The ship that couldn't sink!

10th April, 1912

THIS was to have been a red letter day for Hampshire and, particularly for Southampton. The White Star liner, the *Titanic*, built by Harland and Wolff set sail on her maiden voyage to New York. With a gross tonnage of 46,325 tons, she was the largest and fastest ship in the world; the absolute ultimate in luxury. As she prepared to sail into Southampton Waters, the owners and builders made it clear that they had surpassed even Cunard standards. The *Titanic* was unsinkable — "she was a ship that could not be destroyed".

She set sail for the Atlantic, calling at Cherbourg and Queenstown to pick up more passengers. One man left the ship at Cherbourg on account of a terrible premonition he had experienced and a seaman deserted at the Irish port. There were now 1,400 passengers aboard and 940 members of crew. The ship, carrying 3,418 sacks of mail, steamed westwards, her captain Edward Smith anxious to pick up the Blue Riband for the fastest crossing to New York.

Mesmerized by speed and by the indestructibility of his ship, Captain Smith and his officers ignored radio warnings about the unusually large amount of ice in the North Atlantic. By Sunday the temperature had dropped to 31F (-0.5C), a sure sign that an icefield lay ahead. More warnings were given but the *Titanic* raced on through the night.

The ship struck the iceberg at 11.40 pm. She foundered at 2.20 am — two hours and 40 minutes later. She had nothing like enough lifeboats but even so, many of them were half empty as they were lowered into the water. Nobody knows how many people went down with the ship but the most popular estimate was 1,503. More than 800 were rescued.

The *Titanic's* last moments were terrible for she began to sink at the bow. All her lights went out and her back broke. There was an explosion and she appeared to writhe in agony before plunging down. Wallace Hartley and his bandsmen had been playing to the last and the legend is that their final number was "Nearer My God to Thee".

In Southampton and London a fund for survivors was opened and messages of condolence came from all over the world. It was one of the greatest shipping tragedies of all time.

In days of great deluges the River Test flooded frequently all the way down river to Southampton Water but particularly at Whitchurch, Longparish, Middleton and Wherewell. Dredging of the river was a frequent and necessary activity. Here are the dredgers in action at Longparish in the summer of 1912.

The toll of Shipwreck Coast

ALTHOUGH the loss of the "unsinkable" *Titanic* and the tragedy of those who went down with the ship happened thousands of miles from Hampshire, it made many people nervous about sailing at all, particularly from the area, then simply known as "shipwreck coast". In spite of modern navigational aids, the stormy Hampshire seas, the ledges of Atherfield and Brighstone, the rocks of the Needles and St Catherine were claiming victims regularly.

Some good came out of the recent shipwrecks. The disaster which befell the *Clarendon* stirred the authorities into providing a lighthouse at St Catherine's, first lit in 1840. However, vessels were still driven ashore and the three lifeboats at Brook, Brighstone and Atherfield were kept busy for many years. The loss of the *Sirenia* and the *Eider* were also still very much in people's minds and so too was the *Auguste*, a fine barque of 1,300 tons which ran into a furious gale and quickly broke up, but not before the lifeboats had rescued her crew.

A few years later all hands of the fully rigged ship *Irex* were brilliantly rescued by the local life saving apparatus (LSA) crew working from the cliff top at Freshwater.

What is to be the toll of "shipwreck coast", local people asked, before the menaces are finally lessened?

Bembridge to the rescue

THE Bembridge Lifeboat, on the eastern coast of the Isle of Wight, was frequently called into service. On 3rd February, 1916, led by Coxswain John Holbrook, the lifeboat made four trips to save the 110 crew and pasengers of the *Empress Queen* which had been driven onto the Ring Rocks Foreland. The lifeboat was damaged but the men were brought ashore.

Three years later John Holbrook was involved in another dramatic rescue. The *SS Wakulla* from Los Angeles was floundering in a strong southerly gale and heavy seas but the Bembridge coxswain and his crew saved all the men.

Firemen are busy in Traffic Street, Hilsea.

House collapsed in a storm

December, 1912

MILD weather in winter is often accompanied by rain, wind and murky skies. This was the case in December 1912 when the wind blew in from the Atlantic, sheets of rain drenched the county and, when the sun did appear, it wasn't for very long.

On Boxing Day, a south-westerly gale "of terrific force" stirred the sea into a frenzied state, particularly off the coast of the Isle of Wight. Huge waves crashed over Sandown Parade and the main road to Bembridge was flooded.

At Wellington and Fareham, the flooding was the worst anyone had ever known and a miserable Boxing Day was spent bailing out water from the downstairs rooms of many homes. The water at Lower Quay, Fareham was so deep and forceful that a 20-foot long wall crashed, causing a 20-ton pile of anthracite coal to be swept away. Much of low-lying Portsmouth was awash and trams could not run to Cosham.

Due to the torrential rain and gales, a football match between Portsmouth and Coventry City was abandoned. People in Cowper Road, Kingston were alarmed to hear a thunderous noise and see part of a house collapse. In Portsmouth Harbour there was a collision between the steamer *Solent Queen* and a torpedo gunboat *Niger* but no damage was done.

The only activity on Southsea Common in December, 1912 was one man in a rowing boat.

Sunshine outing and then a bloody war

This car came to a halt by the edge of the flooded road near the Pier Hotel at Portsmouth, while the driver contemplated his next move. This was December, 1912.

THE photograph of the young men aboard the horse-drawn carriage Tally-Ho was taken at Bournemouth on Monday 1st June, 1914 at the beginning of a month in which Hampshire enjoyed more than 250 hours of sunshine. Judging by the smiles on their faces, the men were obviously enjoying their day out, not knowing at the time that Britain was preparing for war and most of them would soon be involved in the bloody events of Europe.

War against Germany was declared on 4th August, 1914 and cheering crowds surged through most towns singing the National Anthem in the belief that offensives would be over by Christmas. The Secretary for War, Lord Kitchener, however, thought the struggle could be a long one and mounted a campaign for at least 100,000 volunteers for a new army. In the Hampshire ports of Portsmouth and Southampton, the Royal Navy was put on a war footing with orders to be prepared to open fire at any moment.

There was nothing exceptional about the summer of 1914. With events in Europe unfolding at a bewildering speed no-one, except seaside traders, gave much thought to the geniality of the weather anyway!

Street boats in the Meon villages

HEAVY rain in the first week of January, 1915 brought serious flooding to the Meon Valley area of West Hampshire. Families at Exton, near Meonstoke were forced to take refuge in upstairs rooms as murky torrents gushed into their homes. Planks of wood were provided for customers of the Shoe Inn but the force of the water was so great that they were carried off towards Corhampton Mill.

Villagers could not get around Exton without a boat and the same form of transport was needed for Corhampton Church. At Soberton, the water rose up to the thresholds of the cottages and the River Meon overflowed its banks right through Wickham.

At Havant, a special committee of the urban council was formed to deal with the problems of flooding in West Street. But it was over the border in Wiltshire where the greatest devastation occurred. Fisherton Street, Salisbury was under three feet of water and a small fleet of canoes and punts took city dwellers on an unusual tour of the submerged area. Salisbury Cathedral was flooded by three feet of water.

The actual date of this picture is not known, but it could have been February, 1917 when the temperature on the Isle of Wight dropped well below freezing and many days' enjoyable skating was possible. The clothes suggest, however, that it was more likely to have been January, 1907, when good skating was also enjoyed at Sandown.

FOUNTAIN IN VICTORIA PARK FROZEN OVER

February 1917 was, in all respects, an unpleasant month. The war with Germany was intensifying, non-military national service was introduced for women and the temperatures plunged to below zero — well illustrated by this frozen fountain in Victoria Park, Landport, Portsmouth. In Russia, where the monarchy was about to fall and there were staggering casualties on the German front, the temperature was 35 degrees below zero.

Chapter Five: 1920 — 1929

A glance at the twenties

1920: After a dull Easter with only two hours of sunshine, a very cool summer followed and the temperature only exceeded 70F (21C) on six days at Ryde, Isle of Wight, with no days reaching this value in July. The warmest day of the year, in fact, was 71F (21.7C) on 4th September. An observer in the Grayshott area said the cool, wet weather in July caused many swifts to depart unusally early.

1921: A complete contrast to the previous year, for this was Hampshire's driest year. There were four absolute droughts of more than 15 consecutive days at Petersfield while the yearly rain total amounted to only 12.73 inches (323mm) at Portchester and 12.75 inches at South Farnborough. At Ryde it was rainless from 31st May to 13th July, a run of 44 days. On 11th July, the temperature reached 88F (31C) and even in October the warmth lingered with 81F (27.2C) on the 4th.

1922: May gave promise of a long, hot summer with nearly half the days rising to 70F (21C) or more along the coast. Sadly the warmth was not to continue and the thermometer reached 70F or more on just four days throughout July and August.

1923: A very wet February with six inches (150mm) of rain in Southampton. A July heatwave sent the mercury up to 94F (34.4C) at Andover as hot air from the Continent swept north-west across Hampshire. On 22nd August at Compton House, near Petersfield, nearly half an inch of rain fell in just 15 minutes.

1924: One of the century's wettest years with nearly 42 inches (1073mm) of rain at Southampton compared to an average 31 inches. However, it was a magnificent Easter with the temperature averaging 65F (18.3C). On Easter Monday there were 12.5 hours of sunshine.

1925: From 30th May to 1st July — 33 days in duration— there was no rain at Ryde. In the Barton-on-Sea area, 313 hours of sun were recorded during June. The rest of the summer, however, was far from glorious!

1926: In a brief cold spell from 13th January, heavy snow fell, reaching a foot in depth at South Farnborough where the temperature plunged to 6F (-14.4C). Winter did not last and February was one of the mildest this century although it was gloomy, with just 48 hours of sun, in the Christchurch area.

1927: A wet year. At Chilland, Winchester, 41.33 inches (1056 mm) of rain fell in the year — a third above the annual average. One of the worst snowstorms on record occurred on Boxing Day.

There was nothing special about the weather in southern England in August, 1924; in fact the holiday season was most disappointing. These visitors to Ventnor, however, appeared to find something to smile about.

Holidaymakers at Ryde, Isle of Wight cool off in the sea on 9th August, 1921. The hot weather continued until early October with temperatures approaching 80F (27C) as late as 5th October.

1920 — 29 (cont)

1928: The lying snow at the start of the year soon melted and January turned out to be milder than usual. In a summer heatwave the temperature reached 88F (31C) in mid-July.

1929: A dry and frosty February — one of the coldest for years with skating on ponds and lakes. By the end of March it was like summer and, on the 30th, Newport was the hottest place in the country with 74F (23C). The year ended on a damp note. In the period from October to January, 24 inches (613 mm) of rain fell around Winchester.

Ringwood was badly flooded in January, 1925 after a brief period of heavy rain.

Salad days of 1921

THE year 1921 was long remembered for its great drought and balmy summer days; a year in which high pressure persisted for week after week and gave such meagre rainfall that in many places it was dubbed "the desert year".

All the spring and summer months were warmer and drier than usual. With a bone-dry countryside and temperatures constantly in the eighties, there were the inevitable fires. Lawns turned brown, flowers shrivelled and farmers became anxious about their stunted crops. The quality of the exhibits at the Twyford Moors fete and flower show on 17th July was so poor it prompted the *Hampshire Chronicle* to write: "Professional gardeners and men who depend upon the industry for their livelihood are having a shockingly lean time this season".

In the plums and turnips class there were no entries at all but there was no shortage of visitors to this event or other outdoor attractions such as the hospital fete at Crowd Hill. Hundreds of people walked miles in the intense heat to enjoy the festivities. The weather was also ideal for the garden fete at East Worldham rectory on 4th August and, at the Romsey fete, there was an exhibition of grapes from a vine planted only 16 months previously at Timsbury Manor.

The parched countryside led to problems for firemen, particularly at Aldershot where a huge blaze broke out on the wooded manoeuvring area of Ash Ranges. This turned out to be the greatest conflagration in the district for many years. A large number of young fir trees was damaged or destroyed and the fire burned for three days. A detachment of the Dublin Fusiliers from Aldershot and members of the Royal Army Service Corps helped firemen tackle the blaze, made all the more dramatic by the setting off of unexploded cartridges.

Grandad's greatest blizzard

25th December, 1927 — 1st January, 1928

CHRISTMAS Day, 1927 was wet. As the rain lashed down in torrents, all prophesies by county weather experts that Hampshire would experience one of those rare and wonderful white yuletides, seemed to fade into a faraway, soggy memory. Few people bothered too much. It was Christmas, and they were at home, playing games with the family.

As evening arrived many would not have noticed that the wind had changed direction to a wicked north-easterly, and that temperatures had fallen to the mid 30's F. Outside in this dark, dank county, Mother Nature was playing her own Christmas game — converting rain into snow and snow into a raging, blinding blizzard.

It began in North Hampshire at 6 o'clock. By 10 o'clock snow was general all over southern England. It was heavy and steady and the accompanying gale force wind whipped the flakes into huge drifts between 12 and 15 feet high. Hampshire awoke to one of the worst snowstorms of the century. Cars were buried, villages isolated, rail lines disappeared, buses were embedded and many passengers stranded.

The *Hampshire Chronicle* said that the inconvenience suffered by the suspension of all traffic was severe especially in Basingstoke, Overton and the Test Valley, the Itchen Valley and the Meon Valley, while many villages such as Alresford, Cheriton, Micheldever and others were cut off completely from the rest of the world.

The *Aldershot News* described the conditions on the Hogs Back, between Guildford and Farnham, as "unbelievable" for the snow on Boxing Day had been whirled hither and thither by violent gusts. "Six inches fell during the night and more inches were added in the morning. Gone were the arrangements made for motoring runs and for visits to distant friends. In their place, snowball fights raged and a *News* representative on a mid-morning tour saw a party of children and adults merrily throwing at an enormous Aunt Sally in whose mouth grotesquely reposed a well-coloured 'meerschaum' pipe. Old toboggans were fished out of their hiding places and new ones hastily constructed and every slope in Aldershot was quickly turned into a run."

The newspaper described the trauma which faced passengers on a double decker bus travelling from Farnham to Guildford. It ran into a snowdrift near the top of Puttenham Hill and, despite superhuman efforts by driver, conductor and a breakdown gang, remained there for 26 hours.

Another couple who attempted to drive from Alton to Winchester on Boxing Day morning found the road reduced to a track about four feet wide with huge drifts either side. They managed to crawl up to the top of Ropley Hill where they saw an array of abandoned cars. Undaunted, they continued to Ropley Stoke only to find the road completely blocked for two miles. With the help of six lads from the village, a rope borrowed from a nearby cottage, a few prayers and a lot of luck, the couple managed to return to Alton by nightfall.

Each area of the county had its own drama. At Winchester on Boxing Day morning, stranded motorists began to straggle back into town having left their cars in drifts. AA road scouts on foot warned drivers "that the roads they proposed travelling on were impassable". At Alresford every road in and out of the town was blocked by huge drifts and the railway system was choked with snow — impassable even to snow ploughs. The same conditions were faced by the people of Basingstoke, Romsey, Petersfield, Andover and Stockbridge.

In rural areas, dairy farmers faced the difficulty of feeding and milking their stock and the greater difficulty of getting the milk into town. They quickly found an answer and by Tuesday, milk was being delivered to Winchester by men pulling sleighs for many miles. At Micheldever, where the snow was 10 feet deep on the main road, a team of eight horses dragged a waggon of milk to the station, more than two miles away. En route the waggon gave lifts to stranded motorists and an intrepid postman. It took seven and a half hours to complete the journey.

By Wednesday more than 2,000 men from the county surveyor's department were engaged in clearing the drifts from between 400 and 500 miles of road in the county. "Expense has not been spared", wrote the *Hampshire Chronicle*. "Lengthsmen have been given authority to engage any men they could get for the emergency, including soldiers and airmen. This has been done readily." The report gave one example of the conditions during this extraordinary week. "To clear a big drift from Butser Hill, 200 men were lorried up from Portsmouth. They dug out 17 motor vehicles, cleared a roadway seven feet wide and after many hours opened the London-Portsmouth road to traffic."

One "never-to-be-forgotten" experience befell a team of estate workers who conveyed the body of a colleague, who had died suddenly, to Cheriton, near Winchester, on Wednesday morning for an inquest. First, they carried the coffin across the fields to a Fordson tractor and then, with a farm wagon, shovels and lamps, they set off from Middle Preshaw across country. The journey to Milbarrows and then through Beauworth village to Cheriton and back took seven

A hard time for the village postman at Littleton, near Winchester, but he has a smile on his face.

A narrow path through the snow in the village of Medstead.

hours.

The Great Blizzard was followed by the Great Thaw. The Hampshire rivers could not meet the demand of the rapidly melting snow and soon most of the low-lying areas of the county were waterlogged. In the Blackwater and Wey valleys it was serious and many homes in the villages of Yateley and Eversley, Ash and Mytchett were inundated. The Basingstoke Canal overflowed its banks between Hartley Wintney and Ash Vale. There was serious flooding in the Test Valley and householders in the village of Longparish were advised to leave their homes.

It was the same in the Itchen Valley. Cottages in Winnall and the Weirs were flooded to a depth of several feet and, in Winchester, firemen were busy pumping water from business premises and hotels. The Petersfield Road at Exton was flooded and, on the Portsmouth Road at Bishop's Waltham, the rapid thaw caused more than 100 tons of earth and several trees to slide forward across the road. The raging floods even threatened the New Forest. An enormous volume of water found an exit via the Lymington River, isolating many communities, particularly Brockenhurst and Beaulieu, Totton and Ringwood.

In London and along the banks of the Thames the thaw was accompanied by an abnormal tide which caused havoc. Many thousands of people were evacuated from their damaged houses but so quickly did the waters rise that 14 people in basement rooms were drowned.

Above: Troops, stationed at Winchester helped to clear a road through the snow during Hampshire's worst winter conditions since 1881.

The telegraph poles look a little lost and so does the dog in this desolate scene at Bentworth, just west of Alton.

Another photograph of the beleaguered village of Medstead, near Alton. This time there is room for a modern car.

With further landslips along the southernmost coast of the Isle of Wight following the great thaw of 1928, it was now becoming clear that more cliff-top cottages would slip into the sea. But nowhere was the erosion greater than at Blackgang where the sea was making inroads at an alarming rate. The photograph above was taken in July, 1928 at Windy Corner, Blackgang after a cliff fall of 250,000 tons.

This is all that remained of the tragic cottages at Bolton's Row, Nether Wallop — struck by lightning on a Saturday afternoon in spring.

The firing of Nether Wallop

5th May, 1928

THUNDERSTORMS sometimes build up out of the blue on a summer's afternoon. In moments they can wreak havoc on one particular spot, while down the road the weather stays dry and sunny.

In early May, 1928, a brief burst of summer weather was enjoyed with the temperature in Winchester reaching a commendable 73F (23C). At Nether Wallop, a small farming village in the west of Hampshire, residents were making use of the fine spell to collect jumble for a sale in the local hall.

On what had been a pleasant Saturday afternoon, evil-looking storm clouds suddenly began to gather over the village just as the Women's Institute opened the village hall for the jumble sale. Minutes later, a violent flash of lightning was to be the cause of great distress with seven Nether Wallop families being made homeless.

The lightning struck the thatch on the picturesque cottages at Bolton's Row in Church Road, starting a blaze which swept through the seven terraced homes. In no time at all they were all engulfed in flames as the fire spread through the roof space. The wooden rafters were soon alight and the tons of thatch burned so fiercely that the roofs soon collapsed.

Many of the occupants were rural workers who toiled long hours to pay for their humble possessions. There was no hope in saving their belongings from the inferno. Among those made homeless were Mrs Price, a widow and her daughter and a Mrs Grace who lived with them, Mr W. Hind, a dairyman and his wife, two sons and a daughter, pensioners Mr and Mrs J. Plank, Mr C. Muspratt, a county council roadman, his wife and two sons, Mr E. Mitchell, a shepherd, his wife, son and daughter, Mr F. Hailstone, an agricultural driver, his wife, two sons and a daughter and Mr H. Harman, a carter, his wife and son.

A neighbour, Mr F. Needham, was one of the first to discover the disastrous fire. He swiftly ran to the row and alerted the occupants. The ladies running the jumble sale abandoned their fund-raising effort to help the victims of the storm. Mrs Guy, wife of the village constable, hurried to the post office to telephone for the Andover firemen. The call was received a minute before 4pm and within 17 minutes the crew had set up a water supply. Another tender arrived from Salisbury.

The kind-hearted folk of Nether Wallop provided emergency accommodation for the stricken families with the exception of the aptly named Hailstone family who were put up by friends in Cholderton.

In Winchester, no rain fell on that fateful day. The warm spell ended within four days and on 10th May, Winchester and the surrounding Hampshire valleys suffered a late air frost with 30F (-1C) being recorded just outside the city.

1929 — hot and cold, wet and dry!

HAMPSHIRE and the Isle of Wight experienced most of the English weather extremes during the variable year of 1929. It began with a fairly settled January and continued with a February that produced almost 150 hours of continuous frost — one of the coldest of the century. Rivers, lakes and creeks froze so solidly that skaters turned out in their hundreds to "all the well-known Hampshire venues and enjoyed many successive days of excellent sport".

March was almost bone dry; in fact less than an inch fell, making it one of the driest ever known. By the time the summer began, rivers and reservoirs were dangerously low and there was much concern over health. By 19th July which was the 136th rainless day of the year, the Metropolitan Water Board suspended the use of water for gardens and motor cars and warned consumers that they faced stiff penalties for waste, misuse or undue consumption.

Nature has a way of compensating and during the last three months of the year, more than 23 inches of rain fell on Hampshire.

Instead of cracked river beds, flood waters were once again surging down the Test, Itchen and Meon valleys.

Chapter six: 1930 — 1939

Focus on the thirties

1930: A severe gale on 12th January caused widespread damage. The end of August was hot, with temperatures in the mid-eighties Fahrenheit. On Saturday 30th August the mercury hit 87F(30C) at Winchester. On returning to Stockbridge Post Office, Longstock's postman, George Prictoe, died from heart failure, due to heat exhaustion. Gale force winds returned on 20th September and the strong gusts fanned the flames of blazing thatched cottages at Red Bridge, Old Basing. There was a glut of plums in the market places but the 'exorbitant' price of 8d a pound in Winchester was criticised. In Portsmouth plums were only 1d to 4d a pound at the same time.

1931: A frosty spell of weather in March. On 10th temperatures were down to 19F (-7C) in Winchester and the warmest that day was just 33F (1C). In July the temperature failed to rise above 74F (23C) all month.

1932: A heatwave was enjoyed in the third week of August. North of Southampton, 89F (31C) was reached on Saturday 20th August. Wet weather drenched the county in October. At Southampton 4.85 inches (123mm) fell at Hudson Verity's Above Bar during the month.

1933: Glorious weather in early August sent the temperature soaring to 90F (32C) on 7th in Winchester. West Meon's Primitive Methodist Sunday School children set off on 4th August in three *char-a-bancs* for a day trip to Littlehampton, travelling through Hambledon, Waterlooville and Chichester. Playing on the sands and bathing "were much enjoyed and the weather was ideal. The party returned very sunburnt", the *Chronicle* reported. December was much colder than normal.

1934: Another heatwave blessed the county in July. For four days in a row, Winchester reported temperatures of 87F (30C) in the second week. On Saturday 7th July, with the mercury at 84F, a heavenly day was enjoyed in the county. December was so mild that many places went through the entire month frost free.

1935: Fine sunny weather provided a perfect day for the Jubilee celebrations in all Hampshire towns on Monday 6th May. King George V's 25 year reign was marked with festivities in nearly every town and village and at Winchester the temperature touched a summer-like 73F (23C). At Preston Candover a pageant by the schoolchildren took place. The sun shone brilliantly and the sky was cloudless. Next day was even warmer at 78F (25C). However, ten days later, on Friday 17th May, night temperatures plummeted and a sharp frost occurred.

Mid-July brought a spell of hot, dry weather. Sunday 14th reached 89F (31C) and the following day, St Swithin's, scorched at 88 degrees. The fine weather brought an abundance of white and meadow brown butterflies.

Sharp frosts were recorded in the three days up to Christmas when it turned milder.

(continued)

Like 1929, the summer of 1933 was a vintage one with more than 200 hours of sunshine recorded in every month from March to September at Ventnor. Picture shows a water carter, collecting what he can from this healthy-looking pond at Chalton, near Horndean.

1930 — 1939 (continued)

1936: An air frost occurred in parts of Hampshire on Friday 29th May when the night-time temperature fell to 32F (0C). On 1st June it dropped to 36F (2C) but by 21st June had soared to a balmy 84F (29C).

1937: A damaging snowfall in early March but a warmer than usual spring and summer. There were temperatures up to 85F (29C) at Winchester on 8th August. A cold December with some heavy snowfalls.

1938: A gale in October put phones out of order, smashed in shop windows and fused street lights but the month was the sunniest at Southampton since 1928. Thick snow lay on the ground as families parted curtains on Christmas morning, 1938 but, although snow fell in parts of the south, in Winchester no snow flakes actually fell on 25th, although the ground was covered in a pretty mantle of white from a heavy fall on 20th. The villages of Droxford and Bishop's Waltham "might have been transferred direct from a Christmas card and the Meon Valley was a beautiful sight with the snow lying on hill and dale, roof and tree," according to the *Hampshire Chronicle*. "Parties were to be seen snowballing, sleighing and ski-ing on the Downs." The Hambledon hunt met in the New Shoe Inn and hounds were followed on foot, owing to the conditions.

1939: The decade ended on a chilly note as cold weather set in after Christmas, heralding the arrival of a bitter spell for the first winter of the second world war.

Tempest was a surprise

12th January, 1930

A GALE of great severity, described by the *Hampshire Chronicle* as "the tremendous hurricane", raged for only a short time on 12th January, 1930 but "will long be remembered for its unprecedented fury".

There was apparently no warning of the tempest and the *Chronicle* claimed that the BBC's customary gale warning was not given, so quick was the arrival of the fearful tempest. In the south of England, practically all roads were blocked by fallen trees and some of Hampshire's finest elms, firs and poplars crashed down.

A train from Bournemouth to Waterloo was hit by a tree at St Cross but miraculously did not leave the rails. There were many other lucky escapes for motorists and pedestrians. In Winchester, a garage at the barracks was demolished by the wild winds and the two cars were blown down a bank nearby. Trees lay across the roads in all quarters of the city and at Abbotts Barton beehives were totally destroyed.

At Hyde Church the weathervane on top of the spire was ripped off along with many tiles. In the Alresford area, 190 trees toppled. At the Bullington crossroads, traffic could not proceed in any direction for many hours because "trees were lying across the various roads in bewildering confusion". At Mr Wilfred Godwin's estate in Compton, nearly 100 trees crashed down in all directions. A much admired cedar tree in the grounds of Southgate House in Winchester was another victim — one of the thousands of specimens mourned. At Oliver's Battery Hen Farm, many chickens were killed after being tossed like leaves by the violent winds. The nearby Club Hall was demolished. "Chairs and tables were smashed, hanging lamps are no longer lamps but masses of twisted metalwork swinging to and fro and relics of Christmas decorations sway in the wind in a pathetic manner. The top of the billiard table was lifted bodily and blown into a field."

At Bournemouth some lawns were covered with sprats washed up by the heavy seas.

Around New Alresford there were many scenes of destruction. Fifty trees were blown down on the Tichbourne estate, 40 at Arlebury and 100 at Old Alresford and Bighton. One woman was injured after being struck on the head by an airborne piece of corrugated iron. The village school at Old Alresford lost its ornamental tall chimneys and pupils were kept at home while workmen fixed tarpaulin sheets over the roof.

The great Sunday gale — which followed two days of rain, sleet, snow and fog — isolated Andover and many other Hampshire towns and villages. Some of Andover's unemployed were given work clearing the many fallen trees.

The storm was the second blow for Avington near Winchester. Just four weeks earlier another gale had felled four majestic trees forming the vista leading northwards from Sir John Shelley Rolls' house at Avington Park. The gale of 12th January brought down another nine.

Many dwelling houses at Chandler's Ford were "considerably damaged" and the river flowing through Droxford overflowed. More than 200 trees fell at Hursley and the "great gale which swept up the Somborne Valley on Sunday night was the worst in the memory of even the oldest inhabitants". About 100 trees were blown down on the Compton estate and a similar figure at Little Somborne Park. The weather vane on the chutrch at King's Somborne was very cock-eyed after that turbulent night. Littleton's oldest inhabitants could not recall a wind of hurricane force before. The clean-up operation in the village was assisted by the fact that the clouds blew away and allowed the illumination of the moon. At Longparish, picturesque cottages had the thatch torn from their roofs. Near the Old House At Home in Overton, six mighty elms crashed in succession across the main road. A dozen more thundered to earth by Quidhampton Mill. In the vicinity of Laverstoke, Ash and Oakley Parks, hundreds of trees "were shorn forever of their glorious beauty".

At Romsey the organist of Shenfield English church was found lying unconscious in the road with his motorcycle some 30 yards away. He had been struck by a falling tree. Near Sparsholt there were scenes of "utmost ha·oc and destruction" on the Lainston House estate and two cows were struck and killed at Crabwood.

Sutton Scotney was badly battered with 100 great elms capsizing in Norton Manor, whilst at Whitchurch, residents girded their thatched roofs with ropes to prevent them being totally stripped. The roof of a cottage in Bell Street was, however, blown off. Hundreds of trees were brought down in Warnford, Westbury, East End and Lipping. The Petersfield to Winchester bus had a lucky escape when trees crashed across the road as it turned round to avoid blocked roads and two London buses had to stop at Warnford all night.

At Wickham a crew member of *HMS Dolphin* managed to squeeze under a fallen trunk in his three wheeler but, sadly, the hood and windscreen were torn off. The driver suffered cuts to his face and was conveyed to Haslar Hospital.

The month of January was mild and Winchester reported 55F (13C) on 15th January.

Record rainfall in a dry year

26th September, 1933

THE summer and early autumn of 1933 were a perfect blend of mellow sunshine, warmth and rainless days, ideal for holidaymakers. The record attendance at Aldershot Open Air Pool of nearly 61,000 bathers bore testimony that it had been an exceptional season. Yet, on Tuesday 26th September a thunderstorm of astonishing severity led to inundations at Fleet while Farnborough, a few miles to the east, remained bathed in sunshine.

The storm raged for more than three hours accompanied by ear-splitting thunder and vivid blue lightning. Roads were transformed into rivers at Hale and Heath End on the Surrey-Hampshire border. Several houses were flooded around Heath End Post Office and the force of the floodwaters was so great that a drain burst with a sound that even drowned the booming thunder. A hole was torn in the road.

The storm moved northwestwards. Eye witnesses in Fleet spoke of the rain falling in sheets and one 70-year-old said he had never known anything like it. He was right, for a rain gauge in the town measured an astonishing 5.16 inches (131 mm), a county record that still stands today.

Floodwaters rushed like a mill race on the Aldershot-Fleet road and huge deposits of silt and gravel quickly blocked the roadway. The following morning saw one resident of St James Road, Fleet digging his pigs out of a sea of mud while in a nearby sty a pig and a number of chickens were drowned. There was a lucky escape for one man, waiting in a horse-driven cart at Church Cookham, when a towering pine tree came crashing down, missing him by just a few inches.

Ironically, Hartley Wintney had been ravaged during the summer and early autumn by many serious heath fires, sparked off by temperatures constantly in the eighties. The countryside had become tinder dry. But now a new element came into play: floodwaters. The main London to Southampton road was like a river and all traffic was abruptly halted. A scene of complete chaos unfolded as motor vehicles wallowed in the surf with firemen trying to push them to the "shore". Shops and houses filled with water and the whole scene was eerily lit by incessant lightning. Several houses at Eversley were struck, one catching fire but no-one was injured.

Perhaps the most terrifying event of the night was experienced by the Hughes family at Winchfield. The torrent of rain had caused a railway embankment to subside sending many tons of earth down onto their bungalow. The family were at home when suddenly the walls gave way, the windows burst, the floor collapsed and the bungalow filled with mud and water. The doorway was blocked and one by one the stunned occupants escaped through a bedroom window.

A photograph taken on the Lyndhurst Road on December 8th, 1937, following a great snowstorm which cut off communications and completely disrupted traffic.

KING WINTER

Scenes like this at Lyndhurst were common in both March and December, 1937.

Telephone wires encased in snow

March and December, 1937

TWO great snowstorms in one year caused chaos in Hampshire. On each occasion the weight of snow brought down branches and lines and put thousands of telephones out of order.

The first blizzard began on on Saturday 6th March, 1937. There were anxious moments for many people, including Mr Edwards of Four Marks who was unable to call the Fire Brigade when his home, St Margaret's, caught fire. He was forced to drive several miles through snowdrifts to reach a telephone that worked. When the Fire Brigade arrived, they realised the nearest water was half a mile back behind them. They turned round but, by the time they set up the hoses, the bungalow had been razed.

In the Basingstoke area, the wet snow lay between six and 10 inches deep and 50 telegraph poles were broken. The lines were encased in clinging snow, three inches in diameter. A train left Basingstoke for Nine Elms at dawn the next morning and at King's Bridge, Newnham, the engine became tangled in fallen telegraph wires which pulled taut and wrenched a pole out of the ground from the top of a bank. The pole hurtled down the slope and struck the train, which was fortunately only travelling at 20 mph.

In Alresford, the snow also damaged electricity cables and many householders were unable to cook their Sunday joints.

Churchgoers, who had paused to marvel at the huge yew trees bent to the ground by the weight of the snow, soon found themselves grateful for the emergency blower which warmed them in the absence of electricity. North of the town, several people had to dig out their cars and some buses were snowbound for many hours.

The melted snow measured 0.65inches (16.5mm) at Winchester. A gale troubled the county later the same day, Sunday 7th March. Its severity in Ropley caused more telegraph wires to be broken and fall across the roads.

There was a repeat performance in December when clinging, wet snow brought down scores of telegraph poles and lines, particularly in the New Forest.

A great snowstorm occurred in December, 1937. It covered the countryside in a wonderful white mantle and made life quite difficult for the delivery men. This picture was taken at Cadnum.

Another photograph showing the effects of the great snowstorm of 8th December, 1937 when main roads were blocked and Hampshire was plunged into darkness by the rupture of power cables. Here a telegraph pole lies across the Lyndhurst Road.

Chapter seven: 1940 — 1949

The wild war-time winters

1940: A severe January with average temperatures below freezing. The sea froze in the creeks and the weight of snow caused the branches of trees to break off. On the Isle of Wight, the temperature fell as low as 11F (-12C). The Thames froze for the first time since the late nineteenth century. June was a sunny, balmy month, a forerunner to a good summer for the battles that raged in the skies during the Battle of Britain.

1941: A very cold January and a cold spring. July produced some warm days but August was notably wet, with 4.82 inches (122mms) at Bishop's Sutton. However, it was the driest year in Winchester for 25 years.

1942: For the third successive January, there were penetrating frosts and also snow. A correspondent, G. Pickthall, writing in the *Hampshire Chronicle* noted that a fieldfare had been driven into Winchester city centre by the 'unusual severity' of the first few days of February. He reminded readers of Thomas Hardy's description of the birds as 'gaunt spectral creatures with tragic eyes - eyes which had witnessed scenes of cataclysmal horror in inaccessible Polar regions.' The year was another dry one with only a fifth of an inch more than the preceding one in Winchester.

1943: The winter, spring and summer were mild. At Whitchurch, where drought conditions occurred during March and June, the temperature reached 88F (31C) on 31st July.

1944: During the five months from 25th January to 24th June, rainfall amounted to only 3.93 inches (100mms) at Winchester. On 31st May, an incredible 91F (33C) was reached at Long Sutton. Weather observer Mr F.E. Box of St Cross, Winchester, was bewitched by the fog and frost at the end of December. He wrote at the time: "Much wet fog was experienced during the month, which, condensing and freezing on the bare trees, produced some beautiful effects as the sun's rays broke through and lit up the ice crystals, festooning the delicate tracery of the branches. This was particularly noticeable on Boxing Day on the high ground on the old Roman Road to Sarum."

1945: January was notably cold. Parts of the south had their second coldest January since 1895. April produced some unseasonably hot weather with 78F (25C) recorded at Winchester by Mr Heathcote Ryde on 18th. Soon after, it became very cold with sleet, snow and hail. Five degrees of frost (-3C) occurred on 30th April. There was heavy thundery rain in central Hampshire in May and June. On 11th May, Hampshire scorched in 83F, but on 19th May, half an inch of rain was measured in an hour at Winchester during a thunderstorm. Christmas was mild.

1947: Great hardships were caused by the long period of snow and frost in the winter and early spring. The Isle of Wight had a temperature as low as 11F (-12C) on 24th February. But nature made amends. The summer was gloriously warm and sunny. Southampton was the hottest place in Britain on 16th and 17th August with 93F (34F).

1948: A remarkable cold snap with heavy snow at the end of February. In some parts of southern Britain the snow lay deeper than at any time in the famous preceding winter. On 20th and 21st February, the temperature failed to rise above freezing during the day and thick snow fell hard and fast in a bitter north-easterly air flow. At Beaconsfield House, Andover Road, Winchester, observer Mr F.B. Heathcote recorded a temperature as low as 11F (-12C) on Saturday 21st. Roads became blocked by snow which had drifted in rural exposed areas. The Cheesefoot Head on the Winchester to Petersfield road had three foot drifts, stopping motor traffic. The Basingstoke to Kingsclere road had almost as much between Shothanger and Woodgarston, while the Alton to Petersfield road was blocked at Round House, Selborne. More than 20 other minor roads were impassable. At Cheesefoot Head, one bus had to be abandoned there for two days despite valiant attempts by the passengers and the crew to clear a passage. Astonishingly, a heatwave occurred within days of the Arctic weather. On 29th February, the mercury soared to 63F (17C) and to 70F (21C) in parts of the south on 9th March. There were reports of people playing snowballs in this heat.

1949: A splendid, sunny spring and summer with much warm sunshine. The sun continued to shine for the King's birthday parade at Aldershot on 9th June. The traditional event had been abandoned during the war years.

Conductors and drivers of these Portsdown double deckers stare, almost disbelievingly, at the road surface following the most famous ice-storm of the century. The road is covered with a shiny glaze, a rare phenomenon in Britain. It was impossible to walk on and certainly impossible to drive.

This winter was a secret!

January, 1940

PARTS of Southern England suffered their coldest January since the Thames-freezing year of 1814. In this first winter of the war, the snow was often heavy, the frost penetrating and, worse still, a supercooled rain fell while the temperature was below freezing point. As the rain hit the frozen ground it covered everything in a varnish-like glaze. The weight of the glaze on telegraph lines at Andover amounted to six and a half tons between posts. Extensive disruption was caused to communication as the wires sagged right down to the ground and snapped. Some of the poles also broke.

Newspapers were unable to carry contemporary reports of the weather, for fear the information would be useful to the enemy. Therefore, stories of the great frost only emerged some weeks later. In the book, *The Weather of Britain* by Robin Stirling, reference is made to the glaze storm at Stonor Hill, Petersfield. 'The ice began to form about 4pm on 27th January and continued the following day with a wind between force four and five on the Beaufort scale, so that all exposed surfaces were ice-covered and windows on eastern and southern sides of houses were stuck fast. During the night of 28th-29th, boughs of beech trees could be heard crashing down all night. The weight of the ice can be gauged from the fact that the wires had one and a fifth inches thick ice on them.'

At Aldershot, thousands of Canadian soldiers — many of them with no military experience, had just arrived as part of the war operations. Within days they were to experience a winter more like the ones they suffered at home. The camp's Victorian barracks were not designed with warmth and comfort in mind, however. One military band found their musical instruments frozen up when they took part in a march at Cove. There were some remarkable stories connected with the ice storm over the West Country. At Cirencester, it rained for two days with a temperature sometimes as low as 25F (-4C). "So complete was the covering of ice that all leaves on shrubs made a noise like castanets rattling in the wind." Many birds perished and rabbits and pheasants could be caught by hand. There were reports that cats were frozen to tree branches and that ponies on Dartmoor had become encased in tombs of ice. Some birds had fallen out of the sky in coffins of ice. Many trees crashed down with great roaring sounds which was unnerving bearing in mind the war had not long started.

On the Isle of Wight, the temperature fell to 11F (-12C) on 21st January. The island suffered badly in this Arctic spell. Roads were made impassable by fallen trees and telegraph poles, while many homes were left without electricity or telephone. The Newport to Cowes railway line was blocked by fallen telegraph poles and passengers had to be conveyed by motor buses. About 80 gallons of milk spilled onto the road at Cemetery Hill, Carisbrooke, when a milk lorry skidded and overturned. All double decker buses were withdrawn as a precautionary measure and no buses ran at all in the Ventnor area. High winds meant that one ferry which left Southampton for Cowes at 6.40pm, did not arrive until 11pm.

This was the desolate scene at Velder Creek, Langstone Harbour in January, 1940 — the middle of "the phoney war", when the whole of Europe was in the grip of an ice age. There was no possibility that Hitler would invade Britain in these conditions.

Two weeks after the snowfall of 16th January, 1940, the Portsmouth Evening News told of the "great transport hold-up, the most chaotic and serious ever known, which goes on and on. All over the country", said the newspaper, "people are marooned, trains are fumbling along their tortuous routes and business is dislocated".

Times were grim in January, 1940. Britain was at war and Hampshire was suffering weather conditions described in the county at the time as "the worst ever known". For these five, however, there were more pressing matters than mere war and weather — where to find a decent slope for a day's good tobogganing! The youngsters are pictured in High Street, Cosham.

The Evening News of 6th June describes the Allied landings.

Bad weather but — "OK, let's go"

D-Day decision: June, 1944

ONE of the biggest military operations in history was almost ruined by the weather. With the date for the proposed invasion of Normandy — scheduled for Monday 5th June, 1944 — just one day away, the wind roared and the rain belted down in torrents. Allied commanders based at Southwick House, Portsmouth were worried. Dare they postpone Operation Overlord ?

They turned to the forecasters who predicted that the weather on the target date would be diabolical with mounting seas, low cloud, poor visibility and more rain. The unavoidable decision was made. D-Day was postponed by 24 hours. Some ships had already left and a few were within range of the German guns by the time they were recalled.

Throughout Sunday, 4th June tension grew to fever pitch. Any further delay would mean shelving the whole operation until tides were once again suitable. A decision had to be taken early on the morning of 5th June. At 3.30 am, when General Eisenhower crossed Southwick's parkland from his caravan quarters to the house itself, he braved "wind of hurricane proportions and rain....travelling in horizontal streaks".

As dawn approached, the weather eased sufficiently for the Supreme Commander to utter his famous words: "OK, let's go". Overlord was under way.

The nerve centre for the operation was Portsmouth's 19th century fortress, Fort Southwick which boasted extensive communications equipment. By the afternoon of 5th June the Channel became a mass of ships converging on the rendezvous point. A vast armada of nearly 7,000 vessels carrying 130,000 men gathered off the southernmost tip of the Isle of Wight, rapidly nicknamed "Piccadilly Circus".

By dawn on 6th June, the invasion force was preparing for the assault on the Normandy beaches, the craft wallowing in heavy seas after a stormy crossing which was marked by seasickness and accidental sinkings. It had been preceded by the dropping of airborne troops into the Normandy countryside in which the weather again played a vital role. It was so bad that the German command believed there was little prospect of invasion and the naval commander actually cancelled the night's E-boat reconnaissance patrols.

During the operation there were many casualties caused by the rough sea and the Allied bombers were hindered by fog and heavy cloud. But, despite the weather, Overlord was a success. The rest is history. The invaders had a foothold in Normandy that was to hasten the collapse of the Nazi regime.

Soldiers reach Omaha Beach after a rough crossing. As the men climbed from their vessels one colonel shouted: "Two kinds of people are staying on this beach — the dead and those who are going to die. Now get the hell out of here."

A snowy afternoon in Southampton on 19th December, 1946. This was the prelude to one of the most severe winters of the twentieth century — and one that no-one living at the time has ever forgotten.

Another photograph of the snowstorm that swept through Southampton on 19th December, 1946. Some weeks later the city was paralysed.

Cruel, bleak winter of 1947

January — March

NOW is the winter of our discontent. Shakespeare's words, written in 1592, could well describe the cruel, prolonged, bitterly cold winter of 1947 when heavy snowstorms and sub-zero temperatures combined with a serious fuel shortage to bring Hampshire to its economic knees.

This notoriously hard winter, in which winds blew from the east due to persistent high pressure to the north of Britain, did not really start until the third week of January — but then it went on and on, throughout February, which was virtually sunless until the 21st, and into March. By that time the war-hardened people of southern England were threatened with even greater shortages of food, emergency regulations, candlelit meals and chaos everywhere.

The bad weather began in mid-January with frost so hard that football matches, including those scheduled for Southampton and Portsmouth, were cancelled. If that was bad news for the men, then there was worse to follow. Thousands of Hampshire workers were made idle by power cuts and the production of beer was cut by 50 per cent. The freezing weather was accompanied by considerable strife. Road haulage workers stopped working leaving thousands of tons of meat rotting in warehouses. The fresh meat ration was reduced to one shilling's worth a week. Bacon, eggs, butter, fish and sugar were scarce; wheat stocks were "uncomfortably low" — and, outside the frost was replaced by heavy snow which piled higher and higher.

The persistent blizzards stopped all shipping in the Channel, creating a new threat to food supplies; fishing fleets were kept in ports and the temperature, on 29th January, slipped to a low of 16F (-9C). The next day was even colder and at Farnborough the grass thermometer measured 1F (-17.2C).

The *Southern Echo* of 30th January told how almost one foot of level snow had fallen throughout southern England and in the more exposed parts of Hampshire many roads were blocked. This news was accompanied by a statement from the Central Electricity Board which said: "It is a very grim tale this morning. The cuts are the worst there have ever been". In Farnborough there was no electricity supply at all as overloading caused two transformers to burn out.

By mid-day on the 30th the Andover to Hungerford bus service was withdrawn because of six foot snow drifts at Rivar Hill and at least 50 Hampshire schools were closed despite a request from the Education Department to "keep schools open as long as possible because fuel stocks are still fairly good".

In Southampton city centre, snow became packed so hard beneath the under-carriage of a tram that the wheels could not grip the rail over Central Bridge. Within minutes eight trams were suffering the same predicament and police had to send an SOS to the Shirley depot for a snow plough in order to get the tram service operating again.

There was chaos, too, in Bournemouth. Trolley buses couldn't grip the rails and frozen points were causing many train delays. The ferry service between Yarmouth and Lymington was cancelled, magistrates could not sit because defendants failed to turn up and, due to the difficulty suffered by boat trains, the *Queen Elizabeth* left Southampton for New York hours behind schedule.

Like Farnborough, Aldershot suffered from a complete breakdown in electricity but soldiers found another way of keeping warm. On 30th January, almost 200 men took part in the Hampshire Military District cross country race. It was run in a snowstorm.

Following a slight thaw which caused serious flooding at Romsey when the River Test overflowed at Greatbridge, the cold weather returned in February with more heavy snow. The *Aldershot News* wrote: "Augmented by German prisoners, Borough Council workmen were kept hard at work throughout the week and all except plumbers were detailed for road clearing duties. Tons of salt were used to melt the snow and this proved so effective that many people thought a thaw had set in again".

By 12th February all shipping in the Channel was stopped again, heightening the fuel and food crisis. As more electricity cuts were introduced, Mr Emmanuel Shinwell, Minister of Fuel and Power said in the Commons that only industrial establishments engaged in essential work were permitted to use current. This did not apply to the Royal Aircraft Establishment at Farnborough where 600 workers were stood off. As the blizzards continued, their families applied to the fuel overseer for extra coal, wood and paraffin but were told these were only allocated to those with extra special needs.

The bitterly cold weather continued through February and so did the fuel crisis. Thousands more in the Hampshire docks, in industry and government establishments were laid off. Even Buckingham Palace and Ministry offices operated by candlelight. Brewers in bottling plants worked their pumps by hand and many other firms used pedal power to keep the wheels of industry turning. More schools closed and so did cinemas. Congregations failed to turn up at churches but thousands flocked to the hills and slopes with their toboggans, particularly to Portsdown Hill, Portsmouth which accommodated hundreds of young people.

By the end of February — the coldest February of the century and one that produced the longest run of easterly winds ever recorded — there was a crisis in the gas industry. For some time pressure had been reduced in accordance with Mr Shinwell's instructions. Now the Southern Utility Company advised the use of "utmost economy to avoid a complete shut down".

As March arrived, this grim winter showed no sign of letting go. Just as power was restored and 800,000 men went back to work, so the snow returned — and this time it was worse than ever. By 6th March, more than 300 major roads in England were blocked and 15 towns were cut off. Road and rail passengers were stranded, villagers had to dig through drifts to reach isolated homes and shipping was stopped again.

In many parts of southern England there were ice storms. A car was welded to the ground near Gatwick, telegraph poles snapped and rain froze on trees turning them into "crystalline stalactites". By this time coal stocks were again dangerously low and, in an effort to boost productivity, the Government announced a ban on mid-week sport. It hardly mattered. No football, rugby or hockey had been played for weeks.

Eventually the long-promised thaw arrived and, just to demonstrate that Mother Nature was still showing her omnipotent hand, it was accompanied by a great deluge and the inevitable floods throughout Hampshire.

This woman shopper in Shirley Road, Southampton shows a determination that was such a remarkable feature of the grim winter of 1947. That determination was the subject of a poem which appeared in the Aldershot News on 7th March, 1947:

How cold and hard, this winter stands,
So trying to us all.
With blizzards blown from other lands,
In icy snow to fall.

Each day brings some fresh attack
That tries to beat us down.
Then frosts that rack, with pipes that crack,
O'ershadows all the town.

But Britain strong, "if resolute",
Can brave these wintry gales.
Then rise again, like King Canute,
And trim old "Hardship's" sails.

Snow clearing at Junction Central, Southampton in January, 1947

There were still many German prisoners of war in Hampshire and some of them were employed to help with the snow clearing — or, as in the case of these four men, making a snowman on Southampton Common.

Those who remember the winter of 1947 still talk about it on occasions. It was bitterly cold, there were heavy snowstorms, there was a fuel shortage and there were strikes. It began in January and by March it had passed into folklore. This scene in Southampton is typical of those bleak days.

Thousands of men were unemployed during the winter of 1947, but not this milkman.
Conditions were tough but he and his horse had an important mission as they plodded around
the streets of Southampton in deep snow.

*Cumberland
Place,
Southampton,
made a
superb ski
run in
January,
1947.*

Three girls complete with bathing hats enjoy the warmth of the sea off Weston Shore, Southampton during the wonderful summer of 1947.

The summer of 1947 was memorable. Day after day the sun bore down from a cloudless sky, reaching a sweltering climax for the August Bank Holiday crowd who invaded the Hampshire resorts. On Saturday 2nd August all accommodation had been booked in Portsmouth and Southsea and there was no more room on the Isle of Wight — but still they kept coming.

The best dry white in England

THE south-facing slopes around Hambledon, which has downland soil similar to that of north-east France, receive a generous share of sunshine. The result is some of the best dry white wine in the country, likened by experts to a still Champagne.

The seed for the foundation of Hampshire's best-known vineyard was sown in France during the first world war when a British soldier, Guy Salisbury-Jones found himself sharing a cold and muddy trench with French comrades. He also shared their wine ration and so began what those grateful soldiers call " a rewarding romance with wine".

In 1949, after a long and distinguished military career, Major General Sir Guy as he became, settled at Mill Down, Hambledon and set out to establish a project near to his heart. Today the famous Hambledon vineyards spread out over the undulating green hills, from where on a clear day you can see the Isle of Wight. Thousands of bottles of Hampshire's finest are supplied each year to the grateful wine merchants of London.

A bumper harvest from the famous Hambledon vineyard.

Crossing the road "a perilous exercise"

EASTER, 1949 was "sunshine all the way". In fact the weather attracted so many visitors to Winchester that the *Hampshire Chronicle* was quite alarmed. "A moving mass of citizens and visitors thronged the High Street on Easter Saturday, establishing a new record. It was almost impossible to forge a way through, and to attempt to cross the High Street was a perilous exercise due to the constant stream of cars passing through the city." The newspaper then drew attention to the proposed Winchester by-pass, "sorely needed despite the great scar it would cause to some of the most beautiful countryside in England."

The hot Easter, in which a reading of 85F (29C) was registered in London was the start of another wonderful summer for Hampshire. July was very hot, particularly on the 12th when the New Forest house, Avon Tyrell, near Bransgore was officially handed over to the National Association of Girls' Clubs by a young Princess Elizabeth.

Another event, only slightly related to the weather, occurred in 1949. On a chilly February night Portsmouth football club won a place in the semi-final of the FA cup in front of a record 51,000 crowd at Fratton Park. They lost the semi-final but went on to win the Division One championship.

Chapter eight: 1950 — 1959

Spotlight on the fifties

1950: There was a heavy snowstorm in the early hours of 25th April as a secondary depression moved south east over Hampshire. Hundreds of silver birch trees snapped in half; raspberry canes four feet high were flattened to the ground. In just over three hours, 15 inches of snow accumulated, accompanied by thunder and lightning. One train took four hours to travel the short distance between Sandown and Newport. At Shanklin it was the heaviest fall since 1908.

1951: The wettest year on record for most of Hampshire. At Privett 58 inches (1481mm) was measured, which is more normal for hilly areas of Devon and Cornwall. During the summer there were some heavy thunderstorms and in one, Cowes received 2.43 inches (62mm) of rain in just 45 minutes, inundating the High Street to a depth of three feet. In many houses small fires were started as water entered fuse boxes. In late December, high winds and tides led to the fire brigade pumping over a million gallons of sea water from the Rock Gardens at Southsea, saving thousands of pounds worth of plants.

1952: A much drier year with rainfall around 30 inches (766mm) at Winchester. There was, however, a heavy snowstorm at the end of March. Lorries had to be pulled out of drifts on the Winchester-Andover road by caterpillar tractors as snow-laden gale force northeast winds swept across Hampshire. One car, marooned all night at Wonston, contained an 80-year-old invalid who, amazingly, was none the worse for her ordeal. The mercury rose to only 33F (0.5C) at Winchester on the 30th, with the temperature remaining below freezing in the Medstead area on the Downs.

1953: The East Coast of England suffered the terrifying tidal surge and inundation of 31st January, perhaps Britain's worst meteorological disaster of the century. The citizens of Hampshire responded with relief aid for the victims and "mountains of clothing and food parcels" were collected. A tropical storm, after crossing Bermuda, headed for Britain and gave Hampshire a buffetting on 21st September and the 83,000 ton liner *Queen Elizabeth* with 973 passengers was storm-bound off the Isle of Wight during the night, before docking in Southampton the next morning. There were some spells of rain, particularly at the end of October when 2.5 inches (62mm) fell during the weekend and there was severe flooding and landslides in Selborne.

1954: On 28th January, the air temperature dropped to 10F(-12.2C) at South Farnborough, with a maximum of 25F(-4C) at King's Somborne. At Winchester the mercury stayed below freezing for six consecutive days with a heavy fall of snow. It was a poor summer and frost whitened the ground on some July mornings! Early September brought the highest temperature, around 80F (26.6C).

1955: January and February were cold with snow lying on 22 days at Long Sutton. Rain turned to snow for a time as late as 17th May. July made up for a poor June with rain on only three days at Winchester and the temperature up to 87F (30.6C) on the 17th. A fine example of a lunar halo was seen at Lymington on 28th November. Christmas was mild with the mercury averaging 54F (12C) by day.

1956: The temperature, which had reached 58F(14.4C) on 27th January at Southampton, plunged to 15F (-9C) on 2nd February as bitterly cold east winds fed in from the Continent. At Long Sutton the mercury fell to just 9F(-13C). Almost every household in Aldershot had frozen pipes and schools closed due to lack of heating and frozen toilets. At a ceremony to cut the first sod in the building of a new cricket pavilion at Hartley Witney, boiling water was used to soften the bone-hard frozen ground. Average temperatures throughout Hampshire remained below freezing for the month of February but it was unusually dry with only 0.08 inches (2mm) at Everton. On 29th July, as a rapidly deepening depression crossed Britain, record wind gusts for July were recorded at several places, including the Hayling Island area, where 78mph was measured.

1957: A mild winter was followed by the warmest March of the century, nearly 6F above average. An extremely dry spring with only 0.68 inches of rain (17mm) in April and May at Hayling Island. In June the sunshine recorder was working overtime at Shanklin with 344 hours of sun and the mercury topped 92F(33.3C) at Blackbushe on 29th. The August Bank Holiday was warm, with the temperature up to 82F (28C) at Leckford and six mile long queues of traffic on coast roads. A fierce storm caused the 2,500 ton vessel *Iano* to run aground at Redcliffe, Sandown on 4th November. . There was widespread damage in Portsmouth and Cosham.

Coldest Easter of the century

1958: March was cold and at Winchester on 12th the air temperature fell to just 18F (-8C). Cold weather continued over Easter, which was the coldest of the century at Ryde and snow lay thickly in Alice Holt Forest on 5th April. It was a poor summer with 10.69 inches of rain (273mm) at Ringwood and with only six days in June and August reaching 70F (21C) at Ryde. People blamed atmospheric atomic tests for the poor weather. It warmed up a little at the beginning of September but the warmth set off thunderstorms which were accompanied by a dazzling and ferocious display of lightning, damaging many buildings on the evening of the 5th. Portchester, Lee-on-Solent, Fareham and Gosport all suffered and at the latter, Christ Church in Stoke Road had its stone cross shattered and hurled 40 yards.

1959: What a contrast to the previous year! Southsea enjoyed its most prosperous season since before the war. Some 220,000 extra deck chair tickets were sold. And with good reason, for there were 78 days above 70F (21C) in Ryde, just across the Solent, and it was the driest summer for two centuries on the Island. Ventnor recorded 1550 hours of sunshine from April to September and it was completely rainless from August 22nd to September 20th.

On 26th April, 1950, a polar depression crossed over south-east England, tugged down Arctic air, turned heavy rain into snow and completely transformed this spring morning. By 7 am, trees were lying across the road, telegraph poles were snapped in half and the Portsmouth to Waterloo railway line was completely blocked by more than six inches of snow. Most of Hampshire was without newspapers because the blizzard was at its worst between 3 and 6am. In Petersfield it was the heaviest fall in 30 years. Power cuts dislocated the county's fire-warning system so Hampshire Fire Brigade put "operation snowball" into action— a system in which each man contacts two others. Picture shows the scene in Cove Road, Fleet.

The Volkerak lay broadside to the shore and took a heavy pounding. Much was salvaged but soon little remained of the Dutch coaster.

When the waves went to work

IT was a cold and stormy night in March, 1951 and the small Dutch coaster, *Volkerak* was sailing up the Channel laden with china clay from Fowey, bound for Amsterdam. She never reached port. In violent seas and poor visibility she was driven ashore just south of Blackgang Chine, Isle of Wight. The crew of eight were lucky. The local life-saving team was quickly on the scene, a line was put over to the *Volkerak* and the men were rescued by breeches buoy.

The ship lay broadside to the shore for several days but the stormy weather persisted, heavy seas were running and she took an enormous pounding. It was obvious she would soon break up.

The salvage men got to work quickly, saved many items of equipment and the cargo but within two weeks the starboard side of the ship was breached wide open. So quickly did the waves go to work that a month later very little remained but a heap of twisted steelwork.

The *Volkerak* was not the only victim of "shipwreck coast" in those stormy days of the early 50's. On Christmas Eve, 1952 the Panamanian steamer *Virginia*, laden with iron ore, went firmly aground on Atherfield Ledge. The salvage operation became a race against time as gales were usually frequent at this time of the year. But the Channel remained calm, the *Virginia* was successfully taken off the Ledge and towed to Southampton for repairs.

In January 1955, in thick fog, the steamer *Kingsbridge* of 7,100 tons went aground on Ship Ledge, Brighstone. After great trouble she was refloated thanks to RN helicopters which were used to put lines on board from a couple of tugs. Two smaller vessels, the *Albatross* and *Claygate* were also grounded in the 1950's, without loss of life.

Gradually modern navigational aids lessened the menace of "shipwreck coast" but the list of victims continued to increase.

The first week of the school summer holidays in 1951 brought a new record to the Isle of Wight — 61,500 passengers making the crossing across The Solent. A few days later they wished they had stayed at home.

In what was described as "the worst floods in living memory", much of the Island was under water and, at Cowes (above) three feet of muddy, brown floods raced through the High Street. The culprit was a thunderstorm which released 2.43 inches of rain in just 45 minutes. An entire terrace of 14 houses in Orchard Road, East Cowes was flooded and small fires broke out everywhere as water entered fuse boxes.

At the height of the storm a fire call came from watchmen in the hangar of Saunders Roe's works where the giant Princess flying boats were housed. Portsmouth was also affected and, at Cosham, water poured down the High Street and mud and silt was found inside the shops.

A heavy snowstorm swept across Hampshire at the end of March, 1952. In some places it turned to glaze as this picture of an avenue in Southampton clearly shows.

A typical summer scene in Shanklin. This picture was taken in 1954, possibly September, when the temperatures hit the eighties after a very poor summer.

A bus and car driver bravely tackle a flooded road at Iford, near Christchurch in July, 1955.

Flood chaos during a July drought

14th July, 1955

JULY 1955 was dry, sunny and warm. It was a month which brought an absolute drought to Cornwall but also triggered violent storms in parts of the South West. In fact, 18th July went into the record books as the day which received the heaviest rainfall in English history — a remarkable 11 inches (279mm) falling in 24 hours at Martinstown in Dorset.

Hurn Airport, near Bournemouth received only a twentieth of this amount but, during an earlier thunderstorm on 14th July, six houses in Southbourne and Christchurch, were struck by lightning. Christchurch Road, Iford (see picture) was badly flooded and motorists had to remove their shoes and socks in order to push cars which had stalled when water swirled around them.

A radio and TV shop at Wimborne Road, Bournemouth, belonging to Mrs G.P. Roberts received a direct hit from lightning which lit up the inside of the shop and welded two vacuum cleaners together. Electricity was "dancing around" the premises.

By 17th July, the hot weather had returned, the temperature soared to 87F (31C) at Southampton and Winchester while, at Alice Holt, near Odiham it peaked at 85F (30C).

The temperature in many parts of Hampshire fell to 15F (-9C) on 2nd February, 1956, freezing a small flurry of snow which had fallen and bringing traffic to a halt. Average temperatures remained below freezing throughout that month.

A torrential downpour in the summer of 1956 brought bad flooding to many areas of north Hampshire. This is Alton High Street by the Swan Hotel — where flooding is a familiar scene to those who know the town well. There were similar inundations in 1945 and 1975 and, on each occasion, firemen had to pump water out of cottages in Mill Lane, Lenten Street, Antsey Lane and the High Street.

Severe storm damages homes

Winds up to 80 mph ravaged the Winchester district on Monday 4th November, 1957, felling trees and causing extensive damage to many homes. There were many power failures at Winchester and telephone communications were disrupted at Botley. In Newton Road, Eastleigh, a side wall of a house collapsed and, at Bursledon, Portsmouth and Southampton (see picture), a tree blew across electricity cables. Friars Hill Dairy at Chandler's Ford was badly flooded and windows in the Royal County Hospital, Winchester were blown out.

There was a terrible ordeal for the crew of the 2,500-ton vessel, *Iano*, which ran aground at Redcliffe, Sandown during the storm. The 19 crew were rescued.

Bonfire night on Tuesday 5th November was a damp squib. More than 1.44 inches (37mm) of rain fell and flooding was extensive once again.

Holiday crowds break Island record

In 1957, the Isle of Wight enjoyed one of its most popular years. There had been nothing special about the summers of the fifties, but 1957 was exceptional and thousands flocked to the holiday isle, especially in June when the temperatures briefly topped the nineties. August Bank Holiday, popular whatever the weather, produced three days of sunshine and the ferries could hardly cope with the traffic. It was estimated that 111,000 people travelled to and from the island during the weekend.

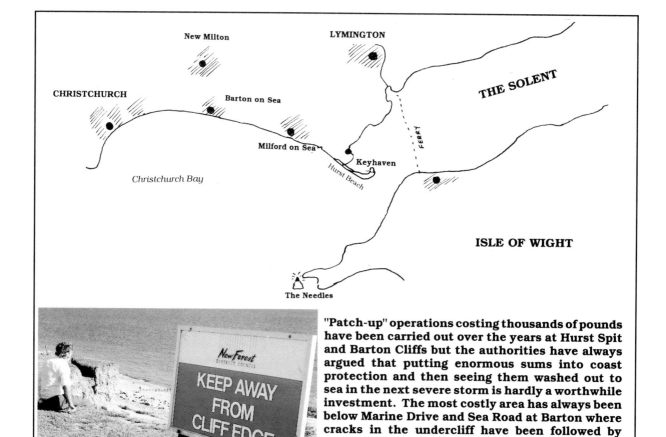

"Patch-up" operations costing thousands of pounds have been carried out over the years at Hurst Spit and Barton Cliffs but the authorities have always argued that putting enormous sums into coast protection and then seeing them washed out to sea in the next severe storm is hardly a worthwhile investment. The most costly area has always been below Marine Drive and Sea Road at Barton where cracks in the undercliff have been followed by great landslides. Homes have disappeared over the edge and others have been threatened.

The cornfield under the waves

MORE storms, more heavy seas, more ferocious winds and more acute the plight of the Hampshire and Isle of Wight seaboard. With fresh landslips at Lymington, Milford and Barton, it became clear that more cliff-top cottages would soon be overwhelmed. Action was needed. The situation was desperate.

One of the greatest trouble spots was at Barton-on-Sea, where houses, huts and gardens were being swallowed into the roaring surf with terrifying speed. In 1953 one householder lost his back garden, his garage and part of the foundations of his house. To make matters worse, property which disappeared over the cliff edge did not qualify for compensation from the local authorities. Insurance companies granted cover only under exceptional circumstances and at a phenomenal premium.

In October 1953, a reporter from the *Hampshire County Magazine* spoke to an inhabitant of Barton who pointed to the grey waters beyond the breakwaters and said: "My grandfather farmed that area — 55 years ago there was a cornfield there". As he spoke a pathway down to the beach collapsed. Posts and rails slithered down amid an avalanche of gravel and mud. More of Hampshire had disappeared.

This, of course, was no new problem. For 5,000 years the south coast of England had been changing because of erosion. It was not sea erosion at Barton, but land erosion, caused by underground streams from the New Forest which were seeping through the topsoil, gravel and sand as far as the strata of clay. In days of great deluges, and there were many in the early fifties, underground rivers were formed. These were undermining the land, sending it crashing into the sea.

As tension along the coastal fringe mounted, the authorities estimated that a protection scheme for Lymington, Barton and Milford alone would cost £289,000. This could not be found — it would be necessary to ask Poole and Portsmouth to contribute, and it was unlikely they would help. In the meantime, the Borough Engineer for Lymington was advised to prepare a scheme to submit to Whitehall.

The sea was making inroads at the rate of several yards a year. It was a slow, painful process but something had to be done to stop Hampshire crumbling into the waves.

The temperature in early February, 1956 fell to 9F (-13C) in parts of Hampshire. Here, at Southampton, a sleeveless dockworker is seen braving the Siberian conditions.

"The north wind doth blow and we shall have snow." This was the bleak scene which faced motorists just outside Winchester on another cold February morning, this time in 1958.

The summer of 1959 was one of the sunniest of the century. The lido at Southampton had never been more popular.

When Hampshire 'liked it hot'

A newly-released film, showing at the Gaumont, Southampton on 5th July, 1959, entitled *Some Like it Hot*, was a perfect way for the city to celebrate the start of a heatwave that was to last, almost unbroken until October. Of course, no-one knew at the time that the temperature was about to zoom into the nineties and that Southampton would, by the first week of October, record 136 days with a reading in excess of 70F.

On Tuesday 7th July, Hampshire firemen dealt with 124 calls, a county record for a single day. The record did not last long. It was broken on 8th July when 141 calls were received — mainly for grass, heath, gorse and woodland fires. One building that blazed was the post office at Braishfield. Bus driver, Roy Carter who was passing, stopped his bus and with help from his passengers tackled the fire with extinguishers until the arrival of Romsey Fire Brigade.

The heatwave ended with a violent storm on 9th July which caused immense damage to crops at Basingstoke. 200 acres of barley were flattened at Lower Wooton in just 10 minutes and, at Andover, hailstones killed two blackbirds and a thrush.

Hot weather returned in August when tourists invaded the county in great numbers. There were so many motoring visitors to the New Forest that the animals were in great danger; in fact by the end of the summer 104 accidents had been recorded, involving ponies, cattle and donkeys. During this month, south coast hotels were packed to capacity and many people were forced to sleep on the beach. There was also an acute water shortage and local authorities in every district appealed to householders to be prudent in using hosepipes.

By September, many wells and reservoirs had completely dried up and, at Sherfield English, near Romsey household water supplies had reached dangerously low levels. Rivers were also running dry, especially the Wallington, above Fareham, the Hermitage, near Havant and the Lymington.

In sharp contrast the chalk streams were still maintaining an ample flow, bearing out the great value to Hampshire of the water-holding chalk strata.

Chapter nine: 1960 — 1969

Weather swings in the 60's

1960: An exceptionally wet end to the summer and a soaking autumn, with October being one of the wettest on record. There was so much mud in Aldershot's Manor Park that the circus could not be held on the first day because it was impossible to get the big top ready in time. *The Aldershot News* wrote: "The whole area was a veritable quagmire with huge channels hewn out of the surface by the immense tractor wheels, making them receptacles for large quantities of water." The rain put up the price of potatoes by 1d a pound to 3d or 4d. Football players all over the county were "saturated to the skin from start to finish" during matches on 8th October and the newspaper described the weather as "most atrocious". It was no better elsewhere. Aldershot Services rugby team visiting Stroud suffered from a mighty gale which blew a covered stand right over the top on to cars parked behind. Some eight inches of rain (200mm) fell in the Farnborough and Aldershot area during October — three and a half times the average. There was no relief in November. Water lay two feet deep in Rectory Road, Farnborough, after heavy storms early in the month and scores of seagulls gathered by the huge lake in Queen's Parade football ground.

1961: Mild weather in February and March was blamed for the huge drop in entries at the Fleet Horticultural Society's first show of the year. Plants were flowering very early and missing the show date. Ice cream sellers trying to cash in on the warm weather were banned from selling their cones at the gates of Farnborough Grammar School, sparking a 'cold war'. A tornado rose from the sea at Bournemouth on 6th October. A witness said: "There was a terrific gust of wind and a roaring noise, followed by thunder and lightning. The tornado ripped most of the roof off a large block of flats on the clifftop and the roof smashed into three hotels, severely damaging them." Subsequent research has shown that most tornados in Hampshire occur in September, October, December or January. They are unknown in April in the county. Most 'twisters' occur in the south of Hants with hardly any north of Winchester.

1962: Snow in early January delighted young Fijiian soldiers visiting Cove. They danced barefoot in the snow at the Royal Engineers' barracks at Southwood Camp. A big freeze set in at the end of December which was to last more than two months. Thick snow fell in the afternoon on Boxing Day and lay on the ground for several weeks.

1963: Well remembered for the long Arctic spell of weather in January and February. On 1st November, a violent tornado struck at World's End near Hambledon. During the late afternoon, witnesses heard a sound like an express train. The whirlwind tore washing off the line and deposited it in a nearby field. It tore the roof off a garage and dropped one half in the road and the other on top of a haystack.

1964: Snow up to four inches deep in the Farnborough and Ash area in mid-January, caused delays to buses run by the Aldershot and District Traction Company and prevented lorries from ascending Beacon Hill, Ewshot. June was a wet month, but it did not dampen the spirits of the 14 scouting patrols camping at the Rushmoor Arena. Their leaders congratulated the boys for their high camping standards "and the excellent spirit shown under difficult weather conditions".

1965: Heavy snow in March lay to a depth of nine inches in North Hants. Fleet mobilised two snowploughs, one bulldozer, eight lorries and four loader shovels to shift the icy layers. Farnborough's local authority sent out six snowploughs and Aldershot six mechanical shovels. By the end of March, warm weather set in and 11 acres of Laffan's Plain near Aldershot went up in smoke.

1966: A large area of high pressure over Scandanavia fed cold air to southern England during January which brought snow, four inches deep in Long Stratton. On 20th January, a thick coating of ice on roads and railways brought transport to a halt and many people came to grief of what they thought were wet pavements. Hospital casualty departments in Hampshire had one of their busiest days ever.

1967: October was extremely wet. Bournemouth collected eight inches or more of rain (200mm) and England as a whole experienced its wettest October since 1903. Six inches of snow fell in Portsmouth after a winter storm in early December which paralysed traffic, particularly on the Sussex side of the county where the falls were deeper still.

1968: Early on 1st July, Hampshire drivers setting off for work found multi-coloured dust speckled over their cars. The dust originated in Spain and North Africa and had been carried north by high level winds and brought down in southern England. The same afternoon was very hot. Liphook sweltered in 93F (34C). Wet and thundery weather followed and there were floods in many parts of south west England. Floods occurred again in mid-September.

1969: An Indian summer was enjoyed at the end of October when Southsea near Portsmouth enjoyed a temperature of 73F (23C). The resort became the warmest place in Britain on 26th.

It was off with the socks and shoes for those hardy people who wished to cross this flooded bridge at Newport on Saturday 1st October 1960 after a violent thunderstorm brought torrential rains to the Isle of Wight.

Newport cut off by raging torrent

THERE was great drama in Newport on 1st October, 1960 when a young mother, Mrs Janette Beverton was being rescued from her flooded home. Janette, carrying her baby, climbed out of her window into the rescue boat which capsized. The raging torrents threatened to carry the couple away but they were saved by a police sergeant. In another incident, Pc Hubble rescued a Newport Corporation boatman who could not swim.

Following torrential rain, Newport was virtually cut off from the rest of the Island. A huge lake formed at the foot of Hunnyhill and residents of Caesars Road and Mill Street were trapped in their houses. The stream, which ran under Hunnyhill bridge, burst its confines and, showing ancient powers, tore away part of the parapet.

The Mew Langton brewery was flooded when a wall collapsed and beer barrels, crates, bottles, crisps and mineral waters were carried downstream.

27th December, 1962 and a massive snowfall causes vehicles to be abandoned in Southampton. This was the shivering prelude to the coldest winter of the century.

Century's coldest winter

December 1962 — March 1963

THE first, feathery flakes fluttered down from a steel grey sky onto a frozen countryside. It was Boxing Day afternoon. Soon they gathered pace and fell ever more thickly and, as light faded on that winter's afternoon, nobody could have envisaged that this snowy shroud would remain until early March across much of Hampshire. The coldest winter since 1740 was under way.

The snow continued for much of the next day, reaching over nine inches in depth at Petersfield and Basingstoke. After an overnight low of 18F(-8C) even Poole Harbour began to freeze over, snaring seagulls in the ice. People away for the Christmas holidays came back to find their homes flooded as pipes had burst. One food store in Southampton had four feet of floodwater. Its location was rather appropriate, Canute Road, but the owner couldn't stop the waves!

However, a worse foe was about to strike. Gathering energy in the warmer waters off Cornwall, a deepening depression was heading towards southern districts armed with masses of fine crystalline snow. The blizzard struck late on Wednesday 29th. It was the worst since 1881 in some parts with visibility down to a few yards. Many roads were soon blocked by towering drifts and cars were abandoned. Over 2,000 calls for help were received by the AA in Southampton. Massive 15 foot drifts covered roads in Petersfield and at the County Surveyor's Department in Winchester they ran out of red headed pins marking the location of blocked roads! Snow ploughing was abandoned late on the 29th between Alton and Fareham, so violent was the snowstorm. Some four miles of the B2150 between Droxford and Hambledon was full from hedge to hedge with seven feet of snow. It took a week to unblock this.

It was chaotic on the Isle of Wight, where even snow ploughs became marooned at Blackgang. Five buses were in deep drifts and one man took all 75 occupants of a stranded coach back to his house for breakfast. At Chale the rectory almost disappeared under a huge drift and the rector himself had to be dug out. However, Hampshire's roads were better than any other county in southern England due to the policy of gritting and salting before the first snowfall, which had prevented it freezing hard onto the roads. The county employed over 500 men, 234 ploughs and 50 bulldozers to combat the snow. In one week 12,000 cubic yards of grit and 4,500 tons of salt were applied to the highways.

Sterling efforts were made by Hampshire's milkmen to deliver the daily pint. One firm in Southampton used eight breakdown crews to keep the vehicles going but everybody received their milk. However, some people had the nerve to telephone and complain about the milk being a few hours late!

No customary thaw followed, indeed the cold intensified during January, the mercury fell to just 5F(-15C) at Long Sutton. Snow lay throughout the month even close to the coast. The Eastney section of Langstone Harbour froze and people could inspect their craft by simply walking out to them. Car ferry services were suspended between Fishbourne and Portsmouth because Fishbourne harbour was frozen over. With the low winter sun as a backdrop, the shores of the Solent looked Siberian with ice floes completing the picture. On land, twenty schools in Portsmouth were closed and over 5,000 pupils sent home due to frozen pipes and lavatories and shortages of fuel. Stocks of shovels, wellington boots and paraffin were sold out from most shops by early January. One of Farnborough's leading suppliers dispensed 1,400 gallons of paraffin in three days.

By February 7th the *Southern Evening Echo* was among many newspapers which were carrying news of a thaw when rain fell. But that was premature. The cold returned with mercury falling to 15F(-9C) on the 25th. Further snow fell and four employees of Aldershot Borough Council collapsed and died in six weeks of snow clearing by mid February. Snow and ice had been so prolonged that Football League teams such as Aldershot Town had not played at home for nearly three months.

This was no doubt the longest duration of cold so far experienced in the twentieth century. Statistics such as 66 days of snow lying at Alice Holt Lodge, 62 in Winchester and even 45 days at Hayling Island on the coast were almost unequalled since the eighteenth century. On the normally mild Isle of Wight there were 68 air frosts at Ryde compared to 44 in 1947 and only two in the 1948-49 winter. With high pressure persistently to the north of Britain and low to the south, incessant winds from Russia and Scandinavia reinforced the old saying "when the wind is in the east 'tis neither good for man nor beast".

After such a severe spell, nature relented and instead of gales and floods that caused so much hardship following the snows of 1947, the temperature rose gradually under a mellow sky of soft sunshine. By the 6th March, Southampton recorded 59F(15C) and crocuses and pansies at Bitterne heralded the approach of Spring. Hampshire was verdant again.

Mr Roger Bartrum who took this picture of Bembridge Harbour clearly remembers the winter of 1962-63. He was a British Rail booking clerk, working late when the blizzard hit the Isle of Wight and it quickly became apparent that he wouldn't be able to get home. He spent the night sitting in the booking office without food or drink. Even the chocolate machines on the station were empty. He managed to get home in the morning, but it was a dramatic journey that took several hours. The picture, which is looking towards St Helen's Quay shows Brading Harbour Yacht Club on the left.

It was possible to walk across the ice at Fareham Creek.

It was fun for some — skating on the lake at Southampton Common in January, 1963.

The last day of December, 1962 and the Basingstoke bus could go no further. Passengers had to alight at Wootton St Lawrence and continue the journey on foot.

Plight of the Forest ponies

FOR the children of Hampshire and the Isle of Wight this desolate winter was great fun. For many adults, too, it brought a challenge to their lives and could certainly be tolerated. For the ponies of the New Forest it was a tragedy — the snow deprived them of much of their normal food. During a bleak winter they are able to survive for some time, but when their food is obscured for week after week, their reserve of fat disappears and they face death. Such was the case in 1963.

When the snow began to fall so thickly on Boxing Day, 1962, the New Forest Association began to plan what could be done for the animals if the snow persisted. They decided that feeding should commence immediately; the RSPCA should take the south of the Forest and Hugh Pasmore, secretary of the Association should look after the north. A large Dutch barn at Lyndhurst was acquired as the central storage depot.

So began one of the most remarkable animal feeding operations in the history of the New Forest. Hugh Pasmore and his vigilantes frequently had to dig themselves out of huge drifts. They quickly discovered that only Landrovers could negotiate the side roads where no snow plough had passed. They established regular feeding points, carrying bales of hay across the snow and their clarion call would bring ponies dashing from all directions, several times a day.

Mr Pasmore, writing in the *Hampshire County Magazine* at the time said: "At first the ponies were suspicious and wary but they soon lost all fear and recognised that we were friends. Eventually we set up seven regular feeding points attracting more than 100 guests to each."

All this cost a great deal of money, but cash help poured in from all over the country, including a postal order from an old lady in Bournemouth who wrote: "It's not a great deal to send you, but it's the best I can do for now".

During those bleak weeks, the New Forest saviours purchased and distributed some 19 tons of hay and straw, while the RSPCA distributed 29 tons. For them the hero was Chief Inspector Lanning. Day after day he slogged around the forest, travelling up to 100 miles at a stretch and never sparing himself. Others went forth daily — children schoolteachers, retired folk, housewives and people on their way to work.

By March, the snows had thawed and their work was done.

The roads were clear but the snow remained until March. This picture was taken near Basingstoke.

Antarctic scene at Droxford, north of Fareham, during the coldest winter of the 20th century.

Red roses for a heroine of the blizzard

THE blizzard which struck the Isle of Wight during the first week in January, 1963 blocked every road and every railway and isolated many villages — in some cases for several weeks. Each day, people struggled against the most tremendous odds to get to work and to clear the roads and railways. Electricity supplies were maintained but the demand was the highest figure ever recorded.

There were many hair-raising stories of endeavour during those extraordinary weeks but none more courageous than that of 19-year-old Christine who was working at Parsonage Farm, Newchurch when it was cut off by drifting snow. Determined to get to work, six miles away, to milk the cows Christine, accompanied by her father, set off at 5 am. There were no hedges visible and

the couple could feel the roofs of cars under their feet as they made their way across this massive white desert. It took five and a half hours to reach the farm. In the evening she left work at 5 pm and got home at 10 pm.

She repeated this incredible journey every day and every evening until the roads were open four weeks later and was nominated by her grandmother in a national competition to find "the heroines of the blizzard". Christine was one of 20 winners and received a bouquet of 12 red roses from Godfrey Winn. Sadly, her grandmother died the day before the winners were announced.

In 1993 Christine, now Mrs Broom, has her own farm at Roud, Godshill, near Ventnor. "I am 49 years-old", she said, " but I would still battle through the weather to attend to my animals."

This remarkable picture of a waterspout was taken by Miss M. Hooke (now Mrs M. Temple) from Alum Bay looking towards Colwell Bay, Isle of Wight on 6th July, 1966. It was seen by ferry passengers crossing from Lymington who noticed "a huge dark cloud, quite awesome and frightening, pointing downwards like a finger". It moved away very slowly.

Tornadoes leave a trail of havoc

THE early 1960's were "the tornado years" in Hampshire. A succession of these rare scourges struck the county, tearing holes in roofs and sending slates soaring in the air like flying saucers.

One was on 1st November, 1963. The tornado hit a house in Rudley Holme, near the aptly named World's End, where Mr Brian Harbord, his wife, parents and grandmother lived. They really thought the world had come to an end as the roof was torn off their garage and a tree uprooted. The tornado then travelled into open countryside, lifting clothes from washing lines on its journey.

Three years later, on 20th October, 1966, another tornado tore in from the sea and damaged several houses in Eastney, near Portsmouth. Cars travelling past the Royal Marines Barracks had difficulty in staying on the road. Two cyclists were lifted from their bikes and pedestrians were blown over. Leaving a trail of destruction, the tornado swept over Eastney bus depot and was last seen moving northwards.

Torrential rains of 1968

14th — 15th September

CARS abandoned, railways flooded, schools closed, September 1968 was one of the wettest months ever recorded in the region and the main drama took place mid-month during the weekend of the 14th-15th. Torrential rain and thunderstorms brought floods to places which seemed immune to such events. Some 2,400 square miles of southern England received in just 48 hours as much as 400 tons of water per acre, with disastrous consequences. The culprit was a deepening depression to the south-west of Britain producing a pronounced trough of low pressure over Hampshire, along which there were large scale vertical motions of the atmosphere. Worse still, it remained stationary for over 24 hours and that meant prolonged, heavy rain.

The deluge of rain caused a bridge to collapse in Godalming, Surrey, completely blocking the main Portsmouth to London railway line. In general there was so much flooding that British Railway officials said they ought to call themselves British Waterways and they urged passengers not to travel. It was just as bad on the roads. The main A3 through Petersfield was shut when the Forebridge at the Causeway was thought to be about to collapse and a local building site off Borough Road, where 16 houses were being constructed, was flooded under several feet of water. The houses were reserved for Naval Officers!

The sudden rising of the flood waters surprised a Sussex man who was out walking and, finding himself surrounded by surging waters, he climbed a tree and frantically waved his handkerchief to attract attention. His distress call was answered by an air-sea rescue helicopter from Thorney Island which spotted him in the tree top and winched him to safety.

It was not only people who were caught out by the rising tide; armies of rats were seen crossing roads near Aldershot as their nests became submerged. A swimming pool at Fleet, recently emptied and cleaned at great expense, was refilled with dirty water overflowing from Fleet Pond.

Lightning hit a house in Fleet, causing hundreds of pounds worth of damage. The occupant, Mr Harry Smith, told the *Aldershot News* reporter that he put up his umbrella, walked outside and found his roof missing!

The eyes of the world's press and aircraft industry should have been viewing the skies over Farnborough on Monday but the flying display at the Air Show was cancelled because the Basingstoke Canal had burst its banks and flooded the runway and surrounding land. Soldiers worked on throughout the night but failed to stem the breach. A Lightning fighter, awash in three feet of water, was towed away and only helicopters and vertical take-off planes could demonstrate to the disappointed crowds.

By Monday 16th, the south of England was described as "a giant lake" by police. Large parts of Farnborough were under water as the swollen Cove Brook overtopped its banks. Just into Surrey, at Ash, 150 people were evacuated, spending the night in nearby halls, some with only their sodden clothing to wear.

Not the ideal start to a honeymoon for an Essex couple who were on their way to Portsmouth when their car was immersed in deep floods on the A3 at Buriton. An RAC rescue van pulled them clear and a local family showed great kindness in entertaining them to lunch while their car dried out.

Rain continued in torrential bursts for much of Sunday and some very large totals were measured. At Long Sutton, south of Odiham, 2.74 inches (70mm) fell and, by the end of the month, 7.4 inches (189mm) had been measured, which was over three times the monthly average. In parts of Surrey, Kent and Essex, rainfall totals of over 5 inches (127mm) were recorded on the Sunday alone, some places having as much as a third of their annual rainfall in just two days. But, as so often happens, a year can make all the difference and Hampshire was to experience in 1969 an extremely dry Autumn. At South Farnborough, September brought only 0.6 inch (15mm) of rain and October 0.2 inch (5mm).

DESERT AND DELUGES

THE year 1968 was famous for other remarkable storms and deluges. On 26th-27th March, when South Farnborough was enjoying temperatures up to 70F (21C), north-west Scotland was being swamped by rainfall approaching 10 inches (254mm). On 1st July, the thermometer soared to 94F (34.4C) at Liphook and an estimated 5,000 tons of the Sahara Desert fell on southern England in the form of a technicolour dust. A few days later, seven people died and many bridges were washed away following a storm that produced 6.85 inches (175mm) at Chaw Stoke. Some 14,000 square miles of Britain experienced more than 200 tons of water to the acre.

THE ALDERSHOT NEWS MILITARY GAZETTE

FARNBOROUGH CHRONICLE

FRIDAY SEPTEMBER 20, 1968   FLEET TIMES AND ODIHAM OBSERVER

A lone policeman stands over the flooded runway at Farnborough Air Display.

FLOOD DRAMA —
150 EVACUATED

MASSIVE mopping-up operations were going on in this area this week after the weekend's 48-hour deluge — worst for 20 years — which left flooded homes, roads, cars and even a flooded swimming pool in its wake.

In two days more rain fell than usually falls during the entire month and it meant different things to different people. It brought
*MISERY to the inhabitants of the Surrey ... houses at Ash ... 150 people were ... ated.

railways — with villages like Tongham completely cut off at times, thousands of commuters stranded on trains and hundreds of cars abandoned on every ...
*A DAY off for chi... Aldersh... ... and
*CANC...
fly...

AT 10.30 am Sunday — torrential ra... high winds down on ... at R... 3...

The front page of the Farnborough Chronicle on Friday 20th September . The floods threatened to cancel the International Flying Display, but hard work by the airmen at Farnborough meant that only one day was lost. Later in the week, the Basingstoke Canal burst its banks for the second time and firemen had to pump out 50,000 gallons of excess water. The canal was then dammed with the fuselage of an old Devon aircraft and scores of people worked to shore up its banks. On Friday (the day of the newspaper), tragedy hit the Air Show when the tailplane of a Brequet Atlantic penetrated the roof of the senior staff mess at Farnborough. Six people — the crew of the Atlantic — were killed.

Iford Bridge, north of Bournemouth, was fast disappearing into the River Stour after many days of torrential rain swamped the surrounding land. This was early November, 1966.

Christmas, 1970 — a winter wonderland

AT last — a white winter wonderland, like the pictures on the Christmas cards. Children who looked out of their windows on Christmas morning, 1968 were certainly delighted. Rain associated with a depression had turned to snow and several inches lay across parts of Hampshire and the Isle of Wight. Families quickly dragged out the toboggans, grateful that they lived in such an undulating county as Hampshire. At Long Sutton, the snow lay for six days.

Two years later in 1970, snow showers fell on Christmas Day covering the ground east of Basingstoke and Alton. For those on the roads on Christmas morning it wasn't much fun. Main routes were fairly clear but others were partly blocked and, for the AA, it was one of the busiest Christmas periods they had ever known.

The table on the right describes some other white Christmases

SNOWY CHRISTMASES IN HAMPSHIRE AND THE ISLE OF WIGHT

1906: Snow began around 10pm on Christmas night and fell thickly for several hours.

1927: Typical snowstorm on Christmas Day, with blizzard-like conditions all of Boxing Day.

1938: Snow fell every day from 16th December until Boxing Day.

1956: An inch or two lay in places as a weather front moved eastwards.

1962: After the coldest Christmas since 1897, snow fell on Boxing Day afternoon and continued for 24 hours. Inland, it did not melt until March.

1981: Snow lay on the ground on Christmas Day from falls earlier in the month.

Chapter ten: 1970 — 1979

A window on the seventies

1970: In what was an average year overall, Southampton excelled in June with its warmest month since records were started there in 1901. Resorts along the south-east coast of the Isle of Wight bathed in more than 300 hours of sunshine. November was wet and particularly so at Ryde with 9.16 inches (234mm) of rain. Christmas was white and several inches of snow lay on the ground, especially over the Downs and hills.

1971: What a contrast to the previous year. Rainfall amounted to almost four times the average in the Christchurch area and four and a half times at Ventnor. A tornado which left a swathe of destruction across parts of London on 25th January, started life as a waterspout off Brook on the Isle of Wight. As it reached landfall on the Island it removed an arm of a signpost and carried it for a mile before wrenching off a roof of a piggery. Nothing more became of it until it reached London two hours later. It was the wettest June in Ryde since at least 1870.

1972: A short, sharp, frosty spell at the end of January gave the south coast its coldest morning for a decade on 31st January. In spite of Liphook reaching a modest 72F (22C) in May, many places had failed to reach 70F by the end of June, possibly due to excessive sea ice off Newfoundland.

1973: One of the driest years of the century with only 18.6 inches (474mm) at Everton, near Lymington — 65 per cent of the yearly average. However, even in a dry year there are invariably some storms and in one a policeman was struck by lightning and temporarily blinded as he was travelling at 60 mph on his motorbike on the Andover by-pass. He managed to keep the bike straight before jumping off. Several houses were damaged in Bournemouth and campsites in the New Forest were abandoned.

1974: Such is the variety of our weather that spring had less than half the average rainfall whilst the autumn and the year in general was wet with a total of 43.9 inches (1122mm) at Lyndhurst. There were some stormy spells during the autumn and on 7th September winds gusted to nearly 70 mph and a fallen tree derailed a train near Liphook but there were no serious casualties. December was mild and, in some parts of southern England, warmer than October with temperatures as high as 60F (15.4C).

1975: The summer of 1975 was memorable for its heat and drought. On 4th August, 93.2F (34C) was reached at Farnborough. At Butser Hill the night of 8th was exceptionally humid and the temperature failed to drop below 66F (19C) — a figure matched at Newport, on 5th. Also on 8th some remarkable thunderstorms occurred and, for a time, 45 flashes of lightning a minute were seen over the sea near Shanklin. Holidaymakers watching the storm clambered to a shelter in the cliffs near Shanklin and huddled together, soaked, as torrential rain bucketed down. Despite this, the Isle of Wight enjoyed its hottest and sunniest August since 1959. There was a tempest on 14th-15th September which shed more than two inches (54mm) of rain on Southampton, making it the wettest September day of the century in the city. The high winds wrought havoc in the Solent and a yachtsman was drowned. Thunderstorms broke out on the Isle of Wight.

1976: A great gale on 2nd-3rd January. Nationally, 24 people died as a result of the storm. January to August was very dry and the summer was memorable for its heatwaves. The Venturers Rescue Operation for Hampshire teenagers helped firemen fight many blazes sparked by the hot weather. The rains came readily in the autumn.

1977: After ther blazing summer of the previous year the mercury hardly rose above 80F (26.7C). On 25th January, there was an unusually sharp fall of pressure across southern England with a sudden dop of six millibars followed by a rise of four millibars in just a few minutes, though the weather remained unchanged.

1978: February brought snow to the west of Hampshire with eight feet high drifts on the hilltops above Winchester, which dislocated traffic for a time and isolated villages but the month ended mildly with rain. On April 10th snow fell and the temperature plunged to 23F(-5C) in the meadows around Winchester. The first national 'May Day' holiday was cold and wet but the Bank Holiday at the end of the month was gloriously fine. Four ground frosts occurred in June. The final month had been very wet with 9.32 inches (238 mm) of rain at Littleton near Winchester and 7.52 inches (193 mm) at Whitchurch. At Bishop's Sutton it was the wettest December since 1935.

1979: The winter of 1978-79 was the coldest since 1962-63. On New Year's Day the temperature fell to a numbing 7F(-14C) at Littleton near Winchester. There was even a little snow on 1st and 2nd May with the temperature down to 27F (-3C) outside Yew Tree Cottage at Littleton.

Blazing summer of 1976

THIS was a summer of parched fields, burning sun and blazing heaths and woods. For 14 consecutive days in June the mercury topped 90F (32C) in southern England following a dry winter and spring. Rivers were reduced to a trickle or dried up completely whilst fires raged across the countryside. The hot sun and blue skies were a boon for the holidaymaker but a nightmare for the farmer and firefighter. Few people would forget this summer.

There was a burst of heat in May. On the 7th the temperature reached 84F (29C) at Grateley, the warmest May day there since 1953. Dry weather in March and April and this early warmth, prompted a spate of heath fires. Smoke and flames rose 100 feet into the air near Blackbushe Airport, forcing the temporary closure of the A30. It destroyed one car and badly damaged two others. But this was only a taste of what was to follow. A weak, warm front moved north east across southern England on 21st June and high pressure settled over the country behind it. Temperatures shot up so that, by 26th, Southampton reached 95F (35C), a national June record. At Hurn Airport there was a run of seven days above 90F (32C), worthy of any Mediterranean resort. By the end of the year, Shanklin had notched up 2,129 hours of sunshine.

Such heat on already parched ground led to a massive outbreak of heathland fires, laying waste thousands of acres and destroying the wild life. Mr Chris Hall of Fleet stated in the *Farnham Herald* that, as he rode back to Fleet, there was smoke everywhere, eight separate columns on the Surrey-Hampshire border. A fire at Thursley had split into three, raging across the common. There were two fires on Ash ranges, two from the Deepcut direction and one from Hook Common. A day later, on 1st July, there was a continuous area of smoke from Ash Common and blazes on Yateley and Blackbushe Commons. The railway was closed near Fleet due to thick smoke over the lines.

A tragic car crash on the M3, where a vehicle plunged into a bridge support at Cove, was made even worse when it caught fire and spread flames to tinder-dry gorse. A man was pulled clear but he died later in hospital. However, the blaze took hold, fanned by strong winds, and a family were evacuated from a nearby house. It was three hours before the situation was brought under control. Elsewhere, Hampshire firemen faced their busiest-ever day. Nearly 500 calls, with 900 men out of 1600 mostly dealing with hot weather incidents. Army units helped with bulldozers to dig fire breaks and supply extra water tenders. Incredibly, during the first twelve days of July there were 1,700 call-outs and some part-time firemen hardly saw their employers.

In those areas that were not burning a new hazard emerged — that of adders. The hot weather meant many more were out basking in the sun and people were warned when out walking not to go barefoot.

An Army Show at Rushmoor Arena turned into a passing out parade for the spectators. According to the *Farnborough News and Mail*, the sweltering heat and the closely packed visitors in their thousands led to hundreds fainting or suffering severe heatstroke. A total of 1,139 casualties were treated. At nearby Farnborough there were troubles of a different kind — running out of beer. Everything liquid was being consumed. Stocks ran dry and toy shops soon exhausted their supplies of paddling pools. Even traffic lights broke down due to the extreme heat in Farnborough, causing traffic jams. Temperatures in control boxes reached almost boiling point.

Water authorities were becoming hot under the collar too. The Mid Southern Authority were able to pump 47 million gallons a day but demand was 49 million and they had to draw on valuable reserves. The normal daily supply is around 37 million gallons. Loud speaker vans toured places such as Aldershot urging drastic cuts on consumption and it became necessary to ban the use of hosepipes

The relentless sun and blue skies inevitably took their toll down on the farm, although initially those areas on heavy moisture-retaining clay, such as near Lockerly, saw combine harvesters out of hibernation earlier than ever before and a wheat yield of two tons per acre. However, at Hartley Wintney it was down to just one ton. Withered and sun-scorched pastures meant that cattle had to feed on winter fodder stocks and one farmer from Hook remarked that it was almost impossible to get any implements into the bone hard ground. The drought was to cost £500 million in lost crops nationally and farm incomes fell by 9 per cent in 1976.

The Ryelaw Garden Flower Show was still a success due to their unstinting labours of gardeners in saving water. Not a drop went down the plug hole; washing up water, water from rinsing vegetables, milk bottles and clothes all went on the garden. Hundreds of gallons laboriously carried by hand. Prize blooms were the result.

Conditions did not improve in August either. Signals from a NOAA-4 satellite 900 miles above Britain on 20th August picked up by the tracking station at Lasham, showed the mainland entirely clear of cloud. As the football season approached, there was anger from local residents, denied the use of hoses for their gardens who saw sprinklers soaking Aldershot football ground. The club argued that the pitch would have become irreparable if unwatered. At the other end of the county, the New Forest was in a dangerous condition and the situation exploded when a fire at Matchams sent a huge wall of flame hurtling along at 40 mph fanned by strong winds. It

Troops assisted in a major blaze at Whitehill, near Longmoor in June 1976. More than 500 soldiers were engaged in a massive fire-fighting operation as the flames spread rapidly.

bore down on a hospital near Ringwood and 360 elderly residents were evacuated, some on beds and others forming a long convoy of wheelchairs emerging from the swirling smoke. One lady spoke of the sky becoming blacker and blacker and there was a terrible smell of burning. At the last minute the wind changed and the hospital was spared. Hundreds more people were evacuated from nearby caravan sites and altogether 250 firemen and 110 soldiers fought to control the blaze using 37 appliances and two 6,000 gallon Milk Marketing Board tankers, commandeered from Dorset to bring extra water. The A31 was closed, causing long delays and every fireman in West Hampshire was summoned, some coming from the beach or church. Trains were halted as embankments blazed and there was no service between London and Bournemouth. On 26th August alone there were 280 fire calls in the New Forest and firemen collapsed from sheer exhaustion. A measure of the unusual conditions prior to the blazing summer was the meagre rainfall from July 1975 to June 1976 at St Catherine's Point on the south coast of the Isle of Wight, where only 12.4 inches (315mm) was recorded, around 50 per cent of the long-term average and estimates from the Meteorological Office put this at a one in five hundred year occurrence. Then, during July and August there were 44 consecutive rainless days at Thorney Island and, by the end of August, conditions were critical. A Minister of

Drought, Dennis Howell, was appointed as, further afield, half a million people in South Wales experienced rota cuts in their water supply and 70,000 people in Devon were placed on standpipe rationing. Damage to buildings as clay soils shrank, leading to subsidence, was estimated to be £60 million, representing 20,000 claims. Ironically, in Hampshire there was a surge of flood incidents when water mains fractured as the ground contracted.

The effects of the drought on flora and fauna was devastating, particularly in the fire ravaged areas. There was concern for the Dartford warbler that nested on the heathlands. In the New Forest alone, it was calculated that 8,000 mature beeches and sycamores died, for they require gallons of water a day during the summer. Probably the greatest tragedy was the loss of millions of beetles, caterpillars, moths, ants and other insects, causing concern about those birds and mammals higher up the food chain in the months ahead.

It seemed as if Nature would not relent as a dry September was forecast. but, suddenly, the weather pendulum swung the other way. Low pressure took up residence close to Britain and bands of rain swept in from the Atlantic. At St Catherine's Point nearly 18 inches (460mm) of rain fell during the Autumn, much more than the previous 12 months! Cracked ground was replaced by flooding. A drought minister had seemed an inspired appointment for the problem was washed away.

Another problem for firefighters and their helpers — this time at Rushmoor, near Farnham,
where a square mile of trees became engulfed in a massive blaze.

February, 1978 at Cheesefoot Hill, near Winchester and a gritting lorry appears over a white horizon, like a mirage.

Children trapped in forest blizzard

FEBRUARY, 1978 was a month that will be remembered for a long time to come, especially by a party of 60 Waterlooville teenagers visiting a holiday training centre at Avon Tyrell in the New Forest during the weekend of 18th and 19th. The county had already experienced very cold weather, for a "high" which had settled over Scandinavia was feeding polar air via the Continent to Britain and by 8th February, snow showers were widespread. Now it was to be accompanied by an intense depression, deepening off south-west Britain and bringing to Hampshire one of the most severe blizzards of the century.

Up to 10 inches of snow fell and much of it was whipped up into enormous drifts. The children at Avon Tyrell, four miles from the nearest village and without electricity, were trapped until a snow plough could cut its way through. So were scores of people in villages throughout southern England.

London-bound commuters from Portsmouth and Havant reached their destination three hours late.

The 5.30 am train had come to a halt at Rowlands Castle with its motors burned out after snow had blocked the cooling vents. A diesel locomotive was sent to push the troubled train through the drifts to Petersfield. It was no better on the roads. Scores were blocked by snow and others by jack-knifed lorries. At Compton, near Winchester, all traffic came to a standstill because of freezing rain falling onto black ice.

The Isle of Wight was described by *The News* as "The Isle of White Out." Police battled for 48 hours to free drivers trapped in snowdrifts and then described the conditions "as some of the worst in living memory". Ventnor and villages in the south were isolated. East Cowes was blocked by cars abandoned by drivers at Whippingham.

In the South West of England the snow was deeper and the blizzard even more intense. On the M4 in South Wales, the main route into the Principality was cut off by drifts of 16 feet.

ISLE OF WIGHT

Weekly Post

anglian
luminium windows
rs and double glazing
RYDE 67226

I·B·C
ST JAMES STREET
NEWPORT 3002
SALE NOW ON

No. 164 — FRIDAY, January 5, 1979 — Price 6p

IT'S THE ISLE OF WHITE

SNOW GO!

Cars and buses abandoned in ten-foot drifts; temperatures well below freezing point and skid-pan driving conditions. These were just some of the New Year hazards Islanders faced after the weekend blizzards which were the worst since the big freeze of 16 years ago.

Though parts of the West Wight were cut off for up to three days, the County Council heeded the warnings of the arctic conditions and staff worked all through Saturday night and Sunday morning to ensure Island roads remained open.

However, some people were caught in the blizzard and abandoned vehicles littered Island roads.

The County Council surveyors' department were warned the snow would fall Saturday night, and set about organizing a 'snow plan.' This meant all the main bus and milk routes were gritted by mid-day Sunday.

is still thick try not to go out unless you have to. The pavements seem more dangerous than the roads."

Island weather expert Mr. Kenneth Hosking said December 31 and January 1 were the coldest days since the big freeze of January and February 1963. The minimum temperature was minus 5.9 degrees centigrade.

More snow pictures, pages

Winchester postmen's great ordeal

LESS than a year later, on 25th January, 1979, Hampshire was again in an icy grip. This time freezing rain combined with snow virtually brought the county to a standstill. In Winchester every road into the city was blocked by vehicles unable to grip on the icy surface. Many people simply abandoned their cars and slithered to work over the ice. The AA said they were receiving 20 calls every 10 minutes.

So chaotic were the conditions that warnings on the radio advised people not to attempt to travel into the centre of Winchester, not even on foot. The situation was aggravated by a strike by council workers which meant that no roads had been gritted before the great freeze. Other industrial disputes were widespread and people began to "stock up" in preparation for a long, hard winter.

As the cold weather continued into February, a Winchester councillor asked his members to spare a thought for the city's postmen whose hands were getting so cold they couldn't undo their fly buttons.

As they needed to use the toilet several times during their rounds in such weather, life was becoming pretty unbearable. Cr. Henry Barnes told the Post Office Advisory Committee that zip fasteners must be fitted to the trousers of all postmen. His motion was defeated.

Black ice and snow continued to plague Hampshire. On 4th February, seven lorries broke down on the Winchester by-pass after their fuel lines froze. A lorry jack-knifed at Sutton Scotney, blocking the A34 and at Morestead, a 16-ton tanker skidded on the ice, mounted a bank and overturned on top of a car close to the Owslebury junction. The woman driver of the car had a miraculous escape.

Others were not so lucky. In the Winchester area alone, dozens of people had to go to hospital after slipping on roads and pavements. A spokesman at the accident unit of the Royal Hampshire Hospital said most were fractures. "We are being kept very, very busy."

Four men in a boat. Rescuers and rescued in the riverside area of Christchurch on 27th December, 1979.

River Stour was like a rapid

27th December, 1979

CHRISTCHURCH and some villages on the Hampshire-Dorset border were devastated by stormwaters which swept down the River Stour like a rapid, following torrential rain. In Blandford, Dorset it was the biggest mop-up of the century as the floods rose higher and higher in the town centre. The great wall of water then raced down the river through Wimborne, forcing people living in the Stour valley to lay sandbags around their homes in a desperate but fruitless attempt to protect them.

The swollen river burst its banks in Christchurch hours earlier than expected and quickly inundated more than 100 homes in 24 roads. About 60 residents were evacuated from the Cara Caravan Park at Iford, many by boat, as their homes were washed away. Within minutes the town was virtually cut off from Bournemouth, only the Tuckton Bridge remaining open. "It was", said the *Bournemouth Echo*, "the worst flood in living memory."

It was the speed with which it struck which took people by surprise. The flow of floodwater down Cedar Avenue was like the Amazon, and far too strong to cross. A contingent from RAF Brize Norton arrived in Christchurch with seven powerful heaters, normally used to warm portable aircraft hangars in the Arctic. Giving out 55,000 BTU's of heat they were quickly used to dry out homes, with more help coming from the 2nd Battalion Green Jackets, stationed at Tidworth.

In Bournemouth, up to 3,000 telephone subscribers were cut off as a result of floodwater.

Chapter eleven: 1980 — 1989

Cold and violent eighties

1980: A quiet, cool January, followed by a very mild February. On 22nd March the temperature fell as low as 19F (-7C) at Hurn near Bournemouth and 23F (-5C) at Newport, Isle of Wight. The summer was poor but not exceptionally bad. It was continuously cool and quite often wet from mid-June to the second half of July. The first three weeks of August were also unsettled, humid and cloudy. This moist air triggered heavy rain on the 12th with 1.75 inches (43 mm) at Ventnor, Isle of Wight. October was cold and November became icy for Guy Fawkes celebrations. There were even some snow showers in southern England on this day.

1981: A bale of straw was thrust up into the sky in a small tornado on 20th October near Pound Gate, Alton. December was very cold and snowy. In Shropshire, England's lowest ever temperature was recorded. This was to be broken within weeks in another remarkable freeze-up.

1982: In January, England experienced its coldest recorded temperature — -15F (-26C) at Newport, Shropshire. In Hampshire, South Farnborough, on the 14th. a reading of just 1F (-17C) was measured, the lowest ever known at this location. Severe thunderstorms moved across the Isle of Wight and Hampshire on 12th July. On 29th August, a ground frost occurred near Farnborough. Tornadoes caused damage near Fordingbridge and in Overton on 9th December.

1983: February ended on a snowy note. On 16th May, a whirlwind struck Romsey. Mrs Phyllis Tanner and Mrs Newman noticed that within minutes of brilliant sunshine it became too dark to read. Suddenly there was a loud clap of thunder, followed by lightning. Looking out of the window of her flat, Mrs Tanner, who wears chromatic lenses, could clearly see the shape of "a great funnel", which came across the old sports ground. Almost at once the branches of trees were "whipped around, plucked up like mushrooms and flung aside." The sun came out in moments and Mrs Tanner took photos of the damage from her bedroom window. A very hot July with some record-breaking heat. Liphook was the warmest place in Britain on 16th July with a sweltering 93F (33C).

1984: The sun blazed down from clear blue skies at Easter, sparking a series of heathland fires around Cove, Fleet and Aldershot. An extensive brush fire swept Minley, south of Yateley, on Easter Monday and the Hampshire Fire Brigade had to draft in 13 tenders to control the flames. Hawley Lake had to be evacuated. Mrs Val Potter, chief instructor at the sailing club, raised the alarm when she saw flames above the tops of trees. A colony of silver-studded blue butterflies was feared to have been wiped out near the Gibraltar Barracks. Friends of the Earth, operating a fire watch from a lookout point at Caesar's Camp, Upper Hale, attended eight outbreaks in one April weekend.

1985: Two spells of cold in January and February gave Hampshire and the Isle of Wight a real taste of winter. Between 12th and 20th January, icy easterly winds blew in from Russia and were accompanied by frequent snow showers. The second cold spell was from 10th February during which part of the Kent coast froze. Lying snow was blown into sculptured drifts in country lanes and hedgerows. At Hurn Airport, near Bournemouth, the temperature fell to 21F (-6C) on 16th January and at Romsey it plunged to 20F (-7C). In February it was perishingly cold, with night-time readings down to 17F (-8C) at Hurn, 15F (-9C) at Romsey and 18F (-8C) at Newport, all on Valentine's Day. Some villages, such as Wootton St Lawrence , near Basingstoke, were almost cut off by drifting snow and a number of homes could only be reached by routes across fields. Frozen pipes in schools such as Wendon Special at Brighton Hill meant an extra holiday for some children. The introduction of a Bobcat pavement snowplough ensured that shoppers in Odiham were not hampered on their missions to get in supplies. At Basingstoke staff at a new automated telephone exchange had to boil kettles and tea urns to get new sophisticated equipment to work. The apparatus was not functioning correctly in the dry atmosphere during the icy snap. In August a man died in an accident off the Needles, Isle of Wight in the gale of 24th. Ryde had a three-week drought in October but the Christmas period was very wet and blustery.

1986: A long spell of frost once again gripped the region in February, ranking it the coldest of the century, bar 1947. The freezing weather set in at the end of January with 18F (-8C) at Romsey and 23F (-5C) at Newport. By 22nd February the mercury had sunk to 12F (-11C) at Romsey and to 18F (-8C) inland on the island, but the month was mainly dry except for a little light snow at times and a heavier fall with up to six inches on the 5th-6th. March started

HOTTEST SUMMERS OF THE CENTURY

1911: The mercury hit the nineties Fahrenheit in August and the year was outstandingly sunny. Totland measured 372 hours of sun in July and 2,115 hours for the year.

1921: The driest year on record and June was rainless at Ryde. The warm, dry conditions lasted into October with 81F (27C) at South Farnborough on the 4th.

1933: Temperatures reached the high eighties Fahrenheit well inland in early August and on 74 days the mercury exceeded 70F (21C) at Ryde.

1947: The summer compensated for the severe winter with the Bournemouth, Christchurch and Lymington area of West Hampshire enjoying average maximum temperatures not far short of 80F (26.7C) during August, reaching 93F (34C) on the 16th.

1949: A long, dry warm summer with 37 consecutive rainless days at Ryde from June 8th to July 14th.

1959: An extremely sunny year, with 2,234 hours of sunshine at Shanklin. May to September was very dry and warm, the latter almost rainless at Leckford.

1975: The temperature peaked at 93F (34C) at Farnborough on 4th August and it was generally the warmest August since 1947.

1976: A long, hot summer with record-breaking heat at Southampton, 96.1F (35.6C). June, July and August all exceeded 300 hours sunshine at Shanklin, with 291 hours in May. Also, Shanklin recorded its driest January, May, June and August. At Thorney Island, there were 44 consecutive days without rain.

1983: July was the warmest month on record, Liphook recorded 92.7F (33.7C) on 16th July and was the hottest place in the UK on no less than 11 days during the month. The average temperature exceeded 68F (20C) virtually everywhere.

1989: A sunny year with over 2,100 hours of sunshine at Ryde. The temperature reached 94F (34.4C) at Romsey on 22nd July. At Ryde the three summer months totalled 889 hours of sunshine.

1990: This summer brought both sunshine, —it was the second sunniest July on record in West Hampshire behind 1911 with over 33 hours — and record-breaking August heat, up to 97.2F (36.2C) at South Farnborough on the 3rd. On the following day, the temperature at Ventnor Park reached 91.2 (32.9C).

1980 — 1989 (continued)

bitterly cold but turned wet. September had an unusually cold day on the 15th with the warmest point being 48F (9C) at Hurn.

1987: A year dominated by the great October storm and a very cold spell in January but there was also a deep and unexpected snowfall overnight on 18th-19th March around Southampton and the Isle of Wight. Level snow was reported as being nearly a foot deep at Cowes, the heaviest fall of March snow here since records began in 1918. There was widespread damage in the New Forest. Tall birch trees were snapped by the weight of the wet and heavy snow.

1988: Mid-summer was very disappointing, for at Southampton the maximum for the whole of July was only 71F (21.5C) and even lower on the Isle of Wight. At Vernham Dean it rained on 25 days but there was at least some compensation for the month with a dreary reputation — November was the sunniest at Ryde since before 1918 with 116 hours of sunshine.

1989: An outstanding year. One of the warmest in the past 300 years. In the Christchurch area it was the warmest of the century so far. At Ryde, 25th June recorded 15.6 hours of sun, the sunniest day since their records began in 1918 and, at Bournemouth, the yearly total of 2,092 hours was the second sunniest of the century behind 1911. Rainfall was the lowest May to September total in Ryde's records with just 4.4 inches (112mm). However, there were less calm moments for a severe gale with winds in the south west approaches gusting to 120 mph swept huge seas towards Hampshire. Lymington suffered some of the worst damage where the town's Bath Road was under five feet of water and the inshore lifeboat was launched to go up and down the road looking for any flood victims on 16th-17th December.

Drifting snow paralyses M3

December 1981 — January 1982

GREAT freeze-ups in the 20th century have often not begun until the winter is well under way. In 1947, it was late January before Jack Frost really took a grip on the county and in 1963 the real snows did not arrive until just after Christmas.

The memorable winter of 1981-2 had a completely different personality. The snow and ice came early in the first week of December, went on until after Christmas, took a break and then returned for a final fling in the second week of January.

Drivers were caught in the first snow when it fell thickly during the morning rush hour on Tuesday 8th December. Before it had a chance to melt, another dose descended on Friday 11th. After this, some remarkably Siberian conditions changed the face of the county.

Blue skies and an incredibly severe frost occurred on Saturday, 12th December. As a striking, rosy sun set over the snow-covered Hampshire Downs in the late afternoon, there was little sign of the gales and blizzards about to bombard the region the following day, but listeners to BBC radio forecasts would have heard the dire warnings.

By early on the Sunday afternoon, snow had spread in from Wiltshire and the south-easterly winds had reached a steady 30mph at Bournemouth. With the temperature only a fraction above freezing, the snow was settling inland but turning to sleet along the coast. Forecasters were now in a dilemma. If the low pressure area, moving in from the south-west, followed the predicted track, it would cause blizzard havoc. However, there were indications that it might travel in a more northerly course than was at first thought. By teatime, the snow had turned to rain at Bournemouth but near Aldershot a blizzard was blowing. Conditions in the northern part of Hampshire were dire. The Queen was caught in snowdrifts in the Cotswolds and off Portland Bill, a freighter was listing at an angle of 45 degrees. Yet, by 8pm it was raining at Bournemouth and the temperature had risen to a quite mild 46F (8C).

Farmers and airmen from RAF Odiham went to the rescue of 56 motorists stranded in their cars in the snow on that stormy Sunday night. The snowbound drivers, including 18 families, found themselves stuck in blizzard conditions at Chalk Pit Hill on the A32 just north of Odiham. The rescuers battled their way through to the cars and guided the occupants to the RAF station where they were given a meal and a bed for the night.

During the gale and snowstorm, televisions went dead when a transmitter on the Hog's Back near Ash blacked out many Southern and London programmes. The A31 linking Surrey and Hampshire was completely blocked and power cuts hit many homes.

Water authority staff worked round the clock to keep supplies going after a spate of burst mains. The Army helped clear roads of snow around Aldershot. In Fleet a gang of 60 men battled to clear snow and ice from roads and the Hampshire County Council depot at Hook took on the mammoth task of clearing 300 miles of the M3. The county put the clearance bill at half a million pounds.

Police in Farnborough received complaints about children throwing snowballs but this problem dwarfed into insignificance against the troubles for motorists in hilly areas.

Homes in Yateley suffered two power cuts in 48 hours. Two thousand properties were without electricity for eight hours on Tuesday 15th December as a result of the weekend's adverse weather which had brought down trees and power lines. On Monday, many schools had suffered further power cuts — especially in Dogmersfield, Odiham and Hartley Wintney. Worst hit was All Saints Junior in Fleet which suffered a gaping hole in the roof, ruined furniture, damaged tiles and a temperature inside as cold as outside.

The sudden thaw following the blizzard caused havoc in schools. A radio announcement had been issued by the county's education office at the height of the snowstorm on the Sunday afternoon advising pupils not to turn up for school. They didn't. The teachers did.

Hart Council's deputy director of administration, Mr Maurice Walthall slipped on ice in Fleet and broke his leg in two places.

The snow eventually cleared and then returned in a showery form in the days leading up to Christmas. The 25th had snow on the ground but was not eligible for a White Christmas title.

In January the weather was to hit the headlines again and South Farnborough was to shiver in the coldest conditions ever known in the town. Snow whipped along by fresh winds brought roads to a standstill again on Saturday and Sunday 9th-10th January. The easterly winds blew the fine snow into drifts up to eight feet deep in the north of Hampshire and seven feet deep on the Isle of Wight. Drivers found 15 minute journeys taking up to two hours. Only one narrow lane of the M3 was open in either direction. At Ewshot, lorries were unable to get up Jekylls Hill. Several big stores around Aldershot, Fleet and Farnborough were out of bread and vegetables because delivery lorries were unable to

Huge drifts piled up on the A3, high on the Downs at Butser Hill, near Petersfield. The snowplough is doing a great job, but has it finally met its match?

Many cars marooned on Isle of Wight

get through. Farmers in rural areas helped clear the snow with tractors and proved a great assistance to the 120 County Council men using 34 excavators and 24 lorries to rid roads of deep snow.

County divisional surveyor, Theo Wellweber, believed that the conditions were "definitely the worst since 1963".

Despite the misery on the roads, there were happy faces on the slopes of Stainforth, Aldershot, where people were out skiing.

On 14th January, South Farnborough had its most severe frost since records began when the temperature fell to a bone chilling 1F (-17C).

Life on the Isle of Wight ground almost to a standstill. On Friday 8th January only the route between Cowes and Ryde via Newport was open. Drifts up to seven feet deep blocked the Freshwater to Newport road. Cars had to be abandoned and island-wide, some 50 cars were marooned.

Storm of crabs and coal

5th June, 1983

A fine day was expected over England. The pressure was high, the month was June and, being a Sunday, an ideal time for a family outing. Instead golf-ball-sized hail, a sky as black as night, violent thunder, falls of coal and fierce squalls that tore down trees made many a day-trip a nightmare experience.

In fact, every lifeboat and search and rescue unit in the Solent area was called out at least once. More than 90 people were rescued in almost 40 separate incidents; typical was that at 12.18pm when 100 dinghies racing at Hill Head were hit by a line squall. The Hamble and Lepe Rescue craft assisted local club officials to tow ashore or right numerous boats. It was a tribute to the rescuers that no-one was seriously injured.

A fresh north-east wind at the surface and strong south-westerlies several miles up, coupled with a layer of cold air in between, is a recipe for severe storms but they were not expected to affect southern England. Gigantic thunderstorm supercells building in Lyme Bay, Dorset swept east along the coast. Dark and menacing clouds produced some memorable skies. One man from Horndean remarked: "A strange cloud appeared from the south, the upper layer was black, about 1,000 feet thick, separated by a cream layer and below a grey patch with a movement like that of a mangle". An hour later Horndean was hit by "monsoon-type" rain and hailstones punctuated by violent lightning and thunder.

It was the hail that many people remembered. At New Milton it resembled snowballs and, at Gosport, a tennis-ball-sized stone appeared to be a conglomeration of smaller ones. An observer at North Bersted said they were like small loaves of bread. One giant hailstone blasted its way through the conservatory roof of a home in Buckland, Portsmouth and knocked a china dog off a sideboard! So many homes and greenhouses suffered perforations that one homecare store in Copnor sold out of its entire 500-sheet stock of corrugated sheeting. At Stamshaw Leisure Centre, Portsmouth, the icy bombardment caused a central section of roof to collapse and then a torrent of rain led to internal ceilings collapsing.

Hailstones are caused when giant cumulo-nimbus clouds grow so high they reach up to where temperatures are well below freezing and the violent up-currents within the cloud whirl ice crystals about. Gathering layer upon layer of ice they finally plunge earthwards. A Wessex helicopter ingested a large hailstone in one of its two engines off Cowes, causing

A scene from a Portsmouth window showing hailstones "bigger than marbles".

it to shut down but it landed safely. The engine was badly damaged.

It was not only hailstones that fell. In the Bournemouth area gardens were littered with coal, the largest measuring nearly three inches across — probably the result of a tornado associated with the storm cloud as it passed over a coal yard. Crabs fell in Sussex coastal towns.

One lady in Portsmouth had a terrifying experience when repairing damage to her conservatory caused by the hail. She was hit by flying house bricks dislodged by a lightning strike on the house next door. She was not badly injured but very shocked by the experience. In Portchester another person was hit by falling bricks as lightning set fire to his loft. 5,000 homes were without power due to blown fuses caused by lightning.

More than an inch of rain fell in many places in a very short time, leading to flash floods. At The Coppice, Horndean, a 40 gallon drum full to the brim with water stood on a manhole cover. It suddenly shot into the air as the pressure of the flood surged through the drains. Garages in nearby Victory Road were inundated twice during the afternoon.

The unexpected deluge from the cumulo-nimbus clouds produced flash floods in many areas of Hampshire and Dorset. This picture which was taken well over the border at Charminster, proved an irresistible choice to illustrate the storm of 5th June, 1983.

Violent thunder and spectacular lightning gave a dramatic display in the night sky "somewhere over the New Forest" on 24th June, 1983.

Tornado havoc near Fordingbridge

POWER lines were brought down, fences flattened, trees uprooted and greenhouses smashed when a tornado spun through the community of Alderbolt, two miles from Fordingbridge, on 9th December, 1982.

A cold front had crossed the Hampshire-Berkshire border at about 9.30 pm, where it wreaked havoc. A mobile home was picked up and moved five feet and several garages collapsed, including one that was brick built. Sheets of timber fencing were blown through the window of a bungalow and one piece punctured the roof.

Various national newspapers blamed the whirlwind as the cause of a rail accident near Fleet when it was found that the tops of trees had been snapped off by the wind and deposited on the line.

At Overton roofs were damaged and summerhouses overturned when the tornado struck. A temporary changing room building at Berrydown football pitch was blown away and one witness, June Barning, told the *Andover Advertiser*: "It sounded like an express train".

The corrugated iron roofs from a block of eight garages were lifted off and carried across a field. A garden shed was turned turtle and a window smashed by a flying slate. The damage was not confined to Hampshire. Over the border in Swallowfield, Berkshire, a whirlwind brought down chimneys, trees and telegraph poles.

The tornadoes occurred during a spell of cyclonic, stormy weather.

Vivid lightning over Andover towards the end of July 1983 signals the end of the heatwave.

Hottest month of the century

A memorable heatwave fell neatly into the calendar month of July, 1983, so that statistically the month became England's hottest ever. It even surpassed the notable Augusts of 1947 and 1959.

Temperatures hit 93F (33C) at Liphook on 16th and 89F (32C) a few days earlier at the Royal Aircraft Establishment, Farnborough.

The warm weather caused the manager of Aldershot Lido to get hot under the collar after vandals repeatedly broke into the pool at night in order to cool off.

Aldershot confectioners ran out of ice cream and had to place chocolate bars in the fridge and Mid Southern Water, not surprisingly, threatened to introduce hosepipe bans unless water consumption was reduced by 10 per cent. In one day an all-time, record-breaking, 61 million gallons of water were used. Vans toured the area urging cut-backs. There were six fires in three days at The Flats country park, Blackwater, and countryside rangers blamed young arsonists rather than the hot sun for the outbreaks.

The heatwave sparked a thunderstorm, which threatened Fleet Carnival. But after 28 years of holding the annual event, organisers were determined not to let the storm dampen people's spirits. However, horse-drawn floats were forced to pull out of the parade. Carnival president Malcolm Arlott told the disappointed participants, "Thunder and horses just do not go together."

More flooding at Christchurch Quay on 25th October, 1984.

Pedal power was needed to get through floods at Copnor Road, Portsmouth in July 1984.

FIVE SEVERE WINTERS

1917: The first four months of the year were very cold with severe frosts and frequent snow. The frost penetrated the ground to nine inches in places. In parts of southern England the temperature fell as low as -4F (-20C).

1940: January was the coldest month for 45 years with average temperatures below freezing except on the south coast of the Isle of Wight. The month was notable for an ice storm when rain fell for 48 hours from the 27th with the temperature below freezing. Near Andover, the weight of ice on wires between posts amounted to more than six tons. Little wonder that damage was severe, many trees lost limbs and windows stuck fast. There were 42 air frosts at Ryde.

1947: As a precursor of things to come, the temperature fell to 8F (-13C) at South Farnborough on 21st December. Winter set in with a vengeance from 23rd January and gave the longest run of easterly winds ever recorded, continuing until 23rd February. The temperature plunged to 2F (-16C) and there was snow on the ground throughout the month. Temperatures averaged some four degrees below freezing on the fahrenheit scale during February.

1963: The coldest winter since 1740. The ground was covered continuously from 27th December through to early March. Snow drifts 12-feet deep isolated dozens of villages in the Portsmouth area and icebergs, four feet thick, tore craft from their moorings in Langstone Harbour. In Fishbourne Harbour, on the Isle of Wight, ships were locked in their berths on the Medina Estuary by hardpacked ice. There were 68 air frosts during this winter at Ryde.

1979: At Overton, the ground was snow covered on 24 days during January and February and the temperature fell to just 7F (-14C) on 3rd January. It was the coldest month since 1963.

The coldest day of the century?

January, 1987

ON Saturday 10th January, 1987, the temperature in northern Europe was falling steadily — to a bitter -26F (-32C) at Helsinki, Finland as a vast area of high pressure settled over Scandinavia. In southern England the stage was set for a memorable cold spell. Everyone wondered — was this year to be another 1947 or 1963?

12th January ranks as probably the coldest day this century in Hampshire. In spite of a good deal of sunshine the mercury stayed well below freezing. Even on the more equable Isle of Wight, the thermometer read only 19F (-7C) at Totland Bay mid afternoon with powdery snow falling.

Set off by chill air passing over the warmer waters of the North Sea and the Channel, thicker snow arrived in the evening. In the north of Hampshire the overnight low plunged to just 12F (-11C). Snow was generally less deep in Hampshire than further east in Kent , Essex and Surrey but strong winds on 14th January blew powdery flakes into large drifts, nearly 10 feet high at Freshwater.

An observer at Totland described the occasion. "The snow blew and it was remarkable to stand in my road watching the drifts develop, a scene rarely witnessed on the Island. By next morning drifts were five feet deep surrounding my house and my car was imprisoned for three days only to be released by a snow plough." Tender plants and palms, normally at home in the Island's genial climate, suffered badly.

A nightmare saved a Basingstoke family from certain death. A young boy fell out of bed due to a bad dream and woke to a home full of deadly fumes as the flue to the solid fuel heater was blocked by snow. The family was taken to hospital suffering from carbon monoxide poisoning.

On a lighter note many of the audience at the Haymarket Theatre, Basingstoke walked out of a controversial play not because they disapproved, but due to the failure of the heating system. The cast carried on bravely, some wearing just flimsy night clothes.

There was controversy of another kind on a national scale as cold weather payments to the elderly were frozen. Although it was bitterly cold on a few days, the average temperature over the week had not reached the threshold level.

Many schools closed throughout Hampshire and the Isle of Wight and thousands of tons of salt were used on snow-bound roads. Temperatures finally climbed slowly above freezing under a pall of cloud which gave no sun at all between 17th and 27th January at Newport. It was a kind thaw, a slow melting with little rain, unlike the stormy conditions which led to such terrible flooding in 1947.

The severe cold did not return but the weather in this memorable year was far from benevolent. There were floods in July, floods in the autumn followed by one of the greatest destroyers of all, which appeared on the horizon in the early hours of an unforgettable October morning.

This waterspout was seen off the coast of Yarmouth, Isle of Wight on 7th August, 1987. Onlookers were fascinated as the spout, which seemed to reach up to the sky, swirled across the waves before fizzling out.

The greatest storm of all?

16th October, 1987

THE people of Hampshire and the Isle of Wight went to bed on the night of 15th October, 1987 comforted by the news that the strong winds forecast earlier in the week were now likely to miss mainland Britain and strike France, Belgium, Holland and the Channel. Certainly weather watchers had been fascinated by the activities in the Atlantic where very cold air moving south from Greenland clashed with warm winds from low latitudes. Low pressure resulted and received added 'adrenalin' from a strong jet stream that included moisture from Hurricane Floyd that had whirled across Florida. The clash of air was violent and all major forecasting agencies in Europe gave loud warnings of exceptionally strong winds.

France was sure the storm was coming her way. "Don't panic but put up your shutters and stay indoors" was the message. In Britain there was no such certainty and, on the night of 15th October, the forecasters under-played the risk of winds but stressed the danger of flood. Southern England, apparently, had nothing to fear.

As Hampshire slept, the Channel seas were whipped up into a great foaming frenzy in which the mariners, caught by surprise, found themselves fighting for their ships — and their lives. All vessels on the move were in danger and many of those in harbour were torn from their moorings and sent careering downwind. The Sail Training Association ship, the *Malcolm Miller*, was anchored half a mile off shore at Cowes but as the storm increased in strength the ship, with 37 trainees between 16 and 24 years old, began to roll and pitch. The wind in the rigging shrieked, the spray made it impossible to see clearly, the dinghy broke away and, according to Captain Adrian Allenby "the crew spent an interesting night".

A few miles away in Southampton, the 400-ton *Barrier* broke from her moorings and nearly went aground, while at Hamble, almost within sight of the *Malcolm Miller*, the 1,400-ton *Sam G* dragged her anchor and ended up on the mud. The havoc at sea was great but it was nothing to what was now beginning to break out on land.

The wind hit the Isle of Wight and the Hampshire coast at 2am. Power cables came down in showers of short-circuiting sparks, tiles flew from roofs and sometimes whole roofs followed them. Caravans were toppled like packing cases. The wind that was going to miss England increased in speed and violence, grabbing all in its path, shaking, twisting, tossing and roaring. Everywhere trees were coming down. They smashed buildings, blocked roads and railways, uprooted telegraph poles and, in the parks and gardens, totally destroyed the work of many centuries.

As the wind reached speeds in excess of 100 miles an hour, the people of Hampshire were suddenly wide awake. At Southbourne and Highcliffe, on the stretch of coast between Bournemouth and the Solent, the roofs on several blocks of old people's flats began to move, then break up. Many of the terrified occupants were evacuated to local community centres.

Across the Solent on the Isle of Wight, county council officials were already creating an emergency centre to co-ordinate efforts. It was estimated that more than 300 trees had fallen across the roads. Homes, hotels, schools and particularly greenhouses were being buffeted by gusts which would find any weakness. In Cowes, coastguards alerted the police when they saw that a boat in the marina had sunk. Inside were a young couple, Norman and Gillian Mitchell and their two children, or so they thought. They were found, sheltering in a public toilet. In Ventnor, a chimney crashed through two storeys of a house in Alpine Road. Mr Peter Stephenson who was in bed in a first-floor bedroom told the *Isle of Wight County Press* that he got the rubble off his bed and felt his way in the darkness along the wall to the door. "If I had gone to the centre of the bedroom I would have fallen through a great hole in the floor. I didn't know it was there."

Near the southernmost tip of the Island, at Blackgang, the two-storey Whitehouse Hotel had its entire roof lifted away. It was not a flat roof but a substantial twin pair of pitched slate roofs with lead sheafing, weighing in the region of 20 tons. The owners, Ken and Rita Smith had spent some time securing windows and doors when the building began to shake. They rushed downstairs as the roof took off and sailed into a field 150 feet away.

By 3 am, Hampshire Fire Brigade began to receive the first calls for help from a bewildered public. More than 50 officers were called in and other staff were summoned from their beds to help man telephones at their headquarters at Eastleigh. The cries of help from the public were continuous. At Hayling Island, a woman was speaking to a fire officer on the telephone when the sea burst into her room in a huge wave. Help was immediately organised. Another call came from Highcliffe, just over the border in Dorset, where a factory fire alarm call had gone off. As the six-man crew drove along the Lymington Road, a tree fell on top of the engine's driving cab. Four firemen in the back were sent flying, later to be admitted to hospital to be treated for minor injuries and shock. The two in the cab, Fireman Graham White and Sub Officer David Gregory stood no chance; they were

A family at Petersfield with the tree which crashed against their home.

killed outright. It took their colleagues an hour to release their bodies from the wreckage.

There were more fatalities on this wild night. Near Salisbury, 18-year-old Anthony Burton was killed when his car struck a fallen tree. Near Petersfield, the body of John Barton, a 35-year-old accountant was found in his crushed car. It took a team of electricity workers several hours to cut him free.

In houses and flats and hotels, families and people living alone waited for the storm to subside. They heard the creak and groan of roofs and walls, the crash of falling chimneys and the incredible noise of the incessant winds which drowned the sound of falling trees. Those who reached for light switches found the electricity had gone so out came the torches, candles and oil lamps.

In the morning, it was impossible to know exactly what had happened. In fact thousands of acres of Southern England were covered in deep thickets of entangled branches and foliage, scorched by the salt wind. In places the debris was so deep it was impossible to see the road and, to make matters worse, the information channels and telephones had been silenced.

The ferocity of the wind was dramatically illustrated at Southampton where the Itchen Bridge was closed to traffic when it was discovered that its expansion joints had swollen to three times their normal size. At Portsmouth Naval Base the screaming winds sent boats skimming out to sea and three tugs spent a hectic night recovering craft. The gangplank of *HMS Newcastle* collapsed and a Royal Navy Helicopter

The wind was in no mood to be charitable! This was a charity shop In Newcombe Road, Fratton.

was scrambled from *HMS Daedalus*, Lee-on-Solent to go to the assistance of a fishing boat reported sinking in the Channel.

In Winchester, the control room of Hampshire police headquarters was choked with calls for help. Extra staff were drafted in, including Chief Inspector Ball, head of the communications department who took three hours to reach Winchester from his home at West Wellow. On his way, with trees still falling, he found all regular routes blocked. His path was eventually cleared by impromptu chain saw gangs, operating as dawn broke. Out in the storm, lone policemen were bearing the brunt of nature's fury. A constable at Burley in the New Forest escaped from his car as a tree crashed on top of it. Another had just left his vehicle on the A303 to deal with a tree-damaged vehicle when his car, too, was hit by a falling trunk. At Bishop's Waltham, a policeman narrowly avoided a corrugated iron shed, flying through the air.

Officers at HQ were working frantically to deal with the remorseless flow of calls. At Barton-on-Sea, residents were trapped when a block of flats partly collapsed. At Totton, near Southampton, serious risk of flooding led to the evacuation of many homes. At 6 am, an inspector from Cowplain asked the control room if it were possible to broadcast a warning because roof tiles "were still flying around like frisbies".

As daylight dawned on the Isle of Wight it was clear the island had been left with damage on a wartime scale. The *Portsmouth News* wrote that "in its wake, the 100 mph horror had left communications in tatters, half the island's homes without power, hundreds of roads blocked by fallen trees and widespread destruction of the countryside. The storm had unleashed its worst in the very early hours, so human casualties as a result were few. Only 13 people were treated for shock and minor injuries."

The greatest casualty on the Island was the 93-year-old Shanklin Pier, which had most of its 1,200 foot length swept away. The shore below was strewn with wreckage while the remains were left teetering above twisted metal spars. As the day wore on hundreds of sightseers arrived, many with tractors and vans, to collect firewood and other spoils. Another casualty was the Ventnor Botanic Gardens on the southern coast where hurricane force winds destroyed more than 100 trees including many rare species.

Stories were now beginning to unfold that were almost too much for the Hampshire and Isle of Wight newspapers to assemble. They included another great drama at sea, for the 935-ton cargo ship *Union Mars* had put out a distress call, three miles south of St Catherine's Point, the rocky headland on the south tip of the Isle of Wight. On passage from Fowey to Rotterdam, she turned round to face the wind hoping to mark time until it moderated. But waves, 40 feet high, smashed the wheelhouse and tore off a door. With navigation equipment lost and lights out of action the ship was being blown towards the cliffs. The Yarmouth and Bembridge lifeboats were alerted.

The ruins of G.A. Day's timber store at Copnor, Portsmouth.

Coxswain of the Yarmouth boat told the *Isle of Wight County Press* that he had never seen seas like this before. "In the Solent, waves were 15 feet high and round the back of the Island, further out to sea, they reached heights of 70 feet." The conditions were so bad that two lifeboats were alerted and mobile shore units at Bembridge and Ventnor instructed to help. The latter didn't get far. As they were leaving town large trees toppled over ahead of them and behind. The rescue workers were trapped.

The *Union Mars* was still in great danger but the wind was now veering to the west and the crippled ship was carried clear of St Catherine's and, under her own power, managed to reach Portsmouth.

Friday 16th October proved to be an exhausting days for thousands of people across Hampshire. One major problem was the lack of electricity across huge swathes of the countryside, prompting the Southern Electricity Board to draft in scores of linesmen from all over Britain to augment its own work force. The workmen had to locate the faults, then isolate them — a task which took several days and in some areas up to three weeks.

British Telecom staff too, were at full stretch. In the month after the storm they had 20, 256 faults to deal with. As with the electricity workers the staff toiled all daylight hours, seven days a week, often soaked to the skin. They were reinforced by men from Scotland, Manchester and West Midlands.

There had been nothing to compare with the cost of the storm in Britain in modern times. As claims from private householders and businessmen started to flood in, the full enormity of that single night of fury began to emerge. The Association of British Insurers estimated that claims were coming in at the rate of 50,000 a day. Hampshire County Council faced repairs of £2.3million and Portsmouth City Council ran up a £2million bill for repairing damage to houses, parks and public facilities. Richard Simmons, the Euro MP for East Hampshire and the Isle of Wight went to Brussels to seek extra financial help from the Common Market disaster fund.

The Meteorological Office explained that this catastrophic event was not a hurricane, but the public looking on the worst damage in 280 years refused to call it anything else. "Why were we not warned", Hampshire demanded. As criticism mounted, the Ministry of Defence commissioned an official report on events leading up to the storm. When it was published it criticised the failure to predict the severity of the storm and the "grossly unfair" reaction from the media.

Hurricane or storm, it was certainly a once-in-a-lifetime event. As the great recovery began in earnest with grants from the Government's Task Force Trees, the people of Hampshire and the Isle of Wight thought they were unlikely to experience such violence again.

Mother Nature had different thoughts....

A gable end crashed through the roof of the Honda Centre in New Road. Portsmouth and completely wrecked these new bikes.

Shanklin Pier, built in 1894 to serve paddle steamers and Victorians on daily excursions, experienced many stormy and precarious years but survived more or less intact for 93 years...until the hurricane. The whole middle section of the pier was carried away by the wind, including the theatre and amusement arcade and more than half its length was devoured by the waves. The next day, hundreds of bewildered sightseers saw tons of debris washed up on the beach — and even more drifting away with the tide.

The glory days of the old pier had long since gone. The salt air was rusting its ironwork, the facilities were run down, the buildings shabby and visitors were few and far between. But in 1986 it was bought by a Southampton leisure company, who had an ambitious development plan to include a disco, restaurant, car park and bathing pool, costing in the region of £4.5 million. They submitted their planning application just a few days before the storm.

Privett Road, Gosport on the morning of the storm — paving stones and trees uprooted

The Big Wheel came crashing down at Beachlands Amusement Park, Hayling Island.

Terror struck in the middle of the night for hundreds of elderly Highcliffe folk as the winds ripped through the roofs of their flats at Greystones, Waterford Road on the cliff-top. Many of the top-floor residents escaped in their night-gowns before the wind tore in. Some were still in their bedrooms when the walls crashed down and spattered them with plaster and glass. Miraculously, none were seriously hurt.

Another Portsmouth telephone box is vandalised — this time by the great wind of 16th October, 1987.

Space-age storm in a marvellous May

The Crimea pub in Aldershot.

MAY 1989 was an outstanding month. The sun shone for 329 hours at Ryde and 319 hours at Romsey. The mercury touched 84F (29C) and rainfall over a large part of Hampshire and the Isle of Wight amounted to less than 0.2 inches (5mm). But this was not the whole story. On 25th May, after a hot and sunny morning, thunderstorms broke out suddenly around lunchtime. Huge cumulo-nimbus (thunder) clouds were clearly visible from weather satellites hundreds of miles out in space. In just under two hours, the equivalent of two months' rain fell in many places. Buildings, and people, were struck by lightning and there was severe flooding.

This incredible storm took time to develop. Thunderstorms were forecast on 24th May but it was not certain where they would strike. The answer was soon evident as the towering cumulus clouds began to grow over north-east Hampshire and within half an hour towered upwards over six miles high. The lightning flashed, the thunder reverberated and a veritable cataract of water poured from the sky, turning roads instantly into rivers.

As much as 2.4 inches (60mm) fell at South Farnborough, much of it in the space of an hour. The busy Cove Road witnessed an unusual scene of a ferry service run by two workers from a local glazing company. They rowed through floodwaters enabling a number of pedestrians to keep their feet dry.

The Wellington precinct at Aldershot was closed as water poured in from Cross Street, lifting up drains and flooding an underpass below the A353 in the town centre. A wall of water tore through gardens in Cranmore Park Estate and sheds were lifted and set down more than 40 feet away in neighbouring gardens. One garage showroom in the High Street had 40 cars "written off". They were parked on the forecourt and the wash from heavy lorries caused them to float and collide with each other. In one extraordinary hour, 150 calls for help were made to the local fire brigade. In Basingstoke and Oakley two homes were destroyed by lightning and electricity pylons damaged.

Remarkably there was a very sharp divide between flood and drought. At Alton, only 0.1 inch (3mm) of rain fell during the whole of July and gardens were withered and cracked by the end of the month.

The Nissan showrooms in Aldershot, where 40 cars were badly damaged.

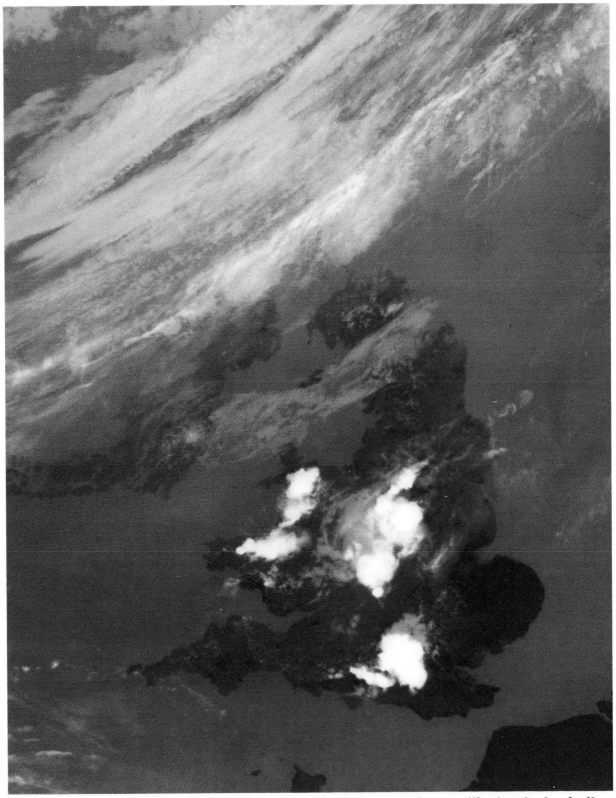

A remarkable photograph of the British Isles taken from a weather satellite hundreds of miles out in space. One mass of cumulus clouds which gathered over north-east Hampshire can be clearly seen. They towered upwards over six miles high.

The highest tide in history

16th-17th December, 1989

AFTER seemingly endless blue skies, hot summer sunshine and a benign autumn, severe gales struck in mid-December, 1989. Winds blew with ferocious force from far out in the Atlantic and a combination of this long fetch from the south west, where waves were reported 20 feet in height, strong winds gusting over 80 mph and huge tides, led to massive flooding along the Hampshire coast and on the Isle of Wight. The depression responsible was code named Low "A".

The far west in Christchurch Bay took a heavier pounding than on the night of the Great Storm of 1987. The Borough Flood Protection Officer, Frank Tyhurst, was amazed to find the tide two feet above an average spring tide, the highest level in recorded history, an entirely unexpected occurrence. Water flooded into Bridge Street and Wick Lane and the entire Mudeford Quay was inundated. A 90-year-old lady slept soundly, totally oblivious of the waters swirling round her bedroom. She was rescued but lost her false teeth.

At Lymington, the sea savagely smashed its way through the sea wall on the Pennington side, breaching it in three places and caused a flood five feet deep. The sea swamped properties in the prestigious waterside area behind the Royal Lymington Yacht Club. Even the 21 foot lifeboat was not immune, for it too had to be rescued when water poured into the boat house, sending it floating up to roof height. The railway line between Brockenhurst and Lymington was closed due to the rising waters.

The inrush of the sea was swift and overwhelming. A car was abandoned so rapidly by the owner that its lights still glowed beneath the water. As soon as the lifeboat was hauled away from danger it was out on the streets with the crew, checking flooded houses for anyone in need of help and rescuing a group of council officials marooned in a car park.

The two mile long shingle spit on which Hurst Castle is perched suffered terribly. Jutting far out into the Solent, it was created by wind and tide and now giant waves were claiming it back tearing out its central section, trapping two fishermen for almost 20 hours. They were eventually airlifted from Hurst Castle. Ironically, £50,000 had recently been spent on sea defences to this enormous natural barrier.

The other side of the Solent was not immune from Nature's onslaught. At Seaview, near Ryde, 250 feet of the sea wall was destroyed and the coast road washed away. One lady told the *County Press* as she

Cars parked on Cowes Parade were marooned in a few feet of water as the sea swept into the town.

surveyed massive blocks of concrete broken from the wall and great mounds of shingle thrown up by the angry sea that, in 30 years she had lived at Springvale Road, this was the worst damage she had seen.

All along the coast the sea made its presence felt. At Yarmouth, water swept through the town, flooding Quay Street and the passenger terminal. A half-filled skip was lifted up and floated around the quay! The town centre of East Cowes was sealed off. House owners, restaurateurs and shopkeepers used everything they could lay their hands on to keep the waves at bay.

Slowly the weather improved and the year ended on a quiet note but this was just the calm before yet another storm.

A breach in the sea defences at Springvale, Seaview, Isle of Wight after the tidal surge of December, 1989.

Sea water surrounded the RNLI headquarters at Lymington on 17th December, 1989.

Chapter twelve: 1990 — 1993

The lost snows of January

1990: Another notable year. A very mild winter was offset by severe gales, the most damaging being on 25th January when six people lost their lives in Hampshire and 47 nationally, the greatest number of weather related deaths since the east coast floods of 1953. Winds were reported near 100 mph on the Isle of Wight.

February was exceptionally mild and the mercury topped 61F(16C) on 23rd, a taste of things to come. At Ryde, April was the sunniest on record. 3rd May was the earliest date that 80F (26.7C) was reached this century in the Christchurch area. Along the coast, July was the second sunniest this century, after 1911 with 332 hours. In August, Romsey recorded 97F (36C).

Staff at the Ordnance Survey Depot in Southampton were told they could start at 6am to avoid the heat! Hosepipe bans were imposed in the Petersfield-Liphook area and there were massive fires in Alice Holt Forest. Hampshire Fire Brigade recorded an increase of 2,000 calls, mainly due to woodland and heathland fires. A 49lb Mediterranean sunfish was caught off Cowes, attracted by the unusually warm waters.

1991: Another dry year but one noted for the wrong type of snow in February, a remark made by a British Rail spokesman when very powdery snow interfered with electrical equipment. Temperatures fell to 14F (-10C) at Romsey and 12F (-11C) at Hurn. Johnny Morris failed to arrive at a reading of 'The Snow Man' in Southampton because his car was stuck in a drift.

Rain in June, which interrupted Wimbledon, was welcomed by fishermen for it refilled some of the county's trout ponds after the dry winter. A cold spell in December, which sent the mercury down to 16F (-9C) in Farnborough, did not presage a cold winter, for mild weather followed.

1992: Rain was in short supply during the first half of the year but July to November gave 24.38 inches (619mm) of rain at Vernham Dean near Andover. About 11 houses were damaged by a small tornado at Chandler's Ford around 6.20pm on June 19th, ripping off tiles and stripping branches from oak trees. The width of the tornado was observed to be about 50 feet, the track was given as south westwards, very unusual for Britain.

1993: Another January devoid of snow. Many places had gone six successive mid-winter months without snow. After a dry February — the third driest this century — May brought some violent thunderstorms. On Wednesday 26th, 2.27 inches (58mm) of torrential rain fell in just two hours at Vernham Dean before dawn. A driver and passenger were making their way along the M27 in a thunderstorm when, suddenly, there was a loud thump and they were travelling upside down. They had collided with a Cessna Citation 550 twin-engined aeroplane, trying to land at Eastleigh Airport, when it aquaplaned on the runway, ran up a bank and smashed through a fence, coming to rest on the carriageway before exploding. Luckily, injuries were not serious and the pilot and co-pilot escaped just in time, as well as the occupants of the car.

17th December, 1989. The waters rushed up the River Beaulieu, causing extensive flooding around the famous village.

Killer storm claims 47 lives

26th January, 1990

WHAT a great variety of extraordinary weather Hampshire and the Isle of Wight had experienced in the last three years — hurricane-force winds in excess of 100 mph, a tidal surge with waves more than 20 feet high, a thunderstorm that produced two months' rain in just two hours, a raging blizzard, damaging floods and drought. As the new decade arrived, many people wondered if Mother Nature could possibly have any more tricks up her sleeve. The answer came on 25th January — a day which dawned with severe weather warnings on radio and television.

A deep area of low pressure was approaching central Britain from the west, the Met Office reported. Winds were likely to gust to hurricane-force 12 on the southern flank of the depression and structural damage could occur. It was a working day. The message, this time was loud and clear.

The storm centre was even deeper than the October 1987 tempest. As it formed in a "jet stream" — a band of fast-flowing winds six miles above the surface of the earth — it deepened rapidly, increased in strength and, like a vandal intent on creating mayhem, headed towards southern England. Hampshire and the Isle of Wight was right in its path.

It struck with the force of a battering ram. Trees, telegraph poles and electricity pylons crashed to the ground, roofs were lifted off, aircraft on the ground overturned, villages cut off and communications crippled. With the day in full swing the casualty list was high and 47 people were killed.

Among them were two workmen who were restoring Uppark House, South Harting, just over the border in Sussex. Site architects advised them to leave but, as they were packing up, part of a temporary roof was lifted off and fell onto the men below. Rescuers had to run to the village for help because their telephone lines were cut and emergency services battled through roads blocked with fallen trees to reach the house.

Another to lose his life was Winchester police Inspector John Smith who died on his way to work at the North Walls station when a tree crashed onto his car at Morestead. A police motor cycle was crushed into the ground by a second falling tree. The Hampshire Assistant Chief Constable, John Wright, who was forced to turn back from the crash scene, said at the time that "these are the most incredible conditions I have ever seen".

At Bassett in Southampton, an elderly man died when a wall crashed on to him in Burgess Road. Eye witnesses heard an enormous explosion and saw 50 tons of brick and rubble just topple over. "The victim", said one, "didn't stand a chance". There was a similar incident on the Stow Estate at Fareham. A six foot high wall crashed down on top of Mrs Lena Marshall of Glenesha Gardens. She died on the way to hospital. At Bishopstoke, near Eastleigh, 86-year-old Lancelot Cross from High Street, Lyndhurst was killed by a branch from a falling tree as he attempted to clear debris from the driveway of a friend's house.

As this dramatic day wore on more tragedies began to unfold. Mrs Louise MacNair, who was visiting the ante-natal clinic at Church Grange, Basingstoke, heard a tree begin to crack and decided to move her car. It was a fatal decision. The tree crashed onto the vehicle and Mrs MacNair died almost immediately.

By the evening when the winds had died down it was believed that Hampshire had lost half a million trees in the storm — similar in total to those felled in 1987. The Woodland Trust described the storm as a "momentous tragedy", while the Countryside Commission, estimating that 60,000 fell in the New Forest alone, said it was "disastrous."

Many historic parks and gardens were also affected. Highclere Park lost valuable cedar and lime trees and more than 200 fell in Hurstbourne Park. Fifteen acres of woodland were flattened at Somborne Park and, tragically, at Selborne, the country's best-known yew tree, aged between 1200-1400 years, was uprooted. There was a macabre sight for those near the scene. In falling it revealed human bones possibly from a pagan burial.

The situation on the roads was chaotic, a tangle of fallen trees, power lines, masonry, overturned lorries and abandoned cars. Hundreds of roads were blocked, including the A272, A34 and A3. In the Petersfield area, police appealed to farmers to come out with chainsaws and snowploughs to help clear more than 100 roads. In the New Forest, not one single road was passable.

Power was cut off in thousands of homes leaving food rotting in freezers. In Liss, Bordon and East Meon, special skips were set up to collect the food. The villages of Froxfield and Selborne were without water because supplies were usually pumped into homes. Right across the county, scaffolding, billboards and road signs were picked up and hurled away by the wind. In one incident there was a serious accident near the M27 interchange at Fareham. Soldiers travelling in an army lorry near Winchester were injured when a tree fell in front of them. At Lasham Airfield, near Alton, 30 gliders were lifted by the wind and hurled across fields and roads.

Dozens of villages were cut off and historic buildings

A pregnant woman, Mrs Louise MacNair from Axford, died when she made the fatal decision to move this car during the storm at Basingstoke.

and barns took a pounding. At Dibden Purlieu's Orchard School in the New Forest, classroom windows were blown out and four children were taken to hospital for treatment. In the Test Valley School at Stockbridge, six pupils were hurt when part of the gymnasium roof was blown off, crashing down on classrooms and cars. Winds ripped Bramshaw cricket pavilion apart and, in Southampton, and Portsmouth dozens of cars in the city centre had their windscreens smashed. People were hurt by flying debris. Motorcyclists and moped riders were blown off their machines. In Salisbury, police rushed out of their headquarters in Wilton Road in a bid to free two people from the wreckage of their car, crashed by a tree. The occupants survived but they were badly hurt.

In Lindford, Mrs Rosemary Haines of Chalet Hill, Bordon, was seriously injured when a tree fell on her car and in Grayshott, Lynette Puttock, of Church Road, Bramshott was trapped by a collapsing brick wall. She suffered severe injuries. In a separate incident in Church Road, Locks Heath, firemen took 90 minutes to free a woman from another crushed car. There were many amazing escapes. The wife of a caretaker at a residential home for the elderly in Bishop's Waltham missed death by seconds when an 80 foot sycamore tree fell inches from her.

By now the trail of havoc was far wider than it had

been during the great storm of 1987, where damage was limited mainly to the South. This time it had begun in Ireland and the West Country and cut a swathe of destruction right up to the North East. Eleven died in Holland and six in France. The Severn Bridge was closed for only the third time in its history. On one stretch of the M27, near Gosport, four lorries were blown onto their sides.

For those at sea it was another terrifying ordeal. On one Fishbourne to Portsmouth ferry, more than 300 passengers spent five and a half hours afloat. The ship somehow crossed the storm-tossed Solent, but had to ride out the tempest in Portsmouth harbour for hours before being able to dock. Red Funnel passengers on the Netley Castle took four hours to travel from Cowes to Southampton and then learned that all other ferries had been suspended. There was so much debris in Southampton Water, including drifting boats and even a Portacabin, it would have been dangerous to continue. Hydrofoil and hovercraft services were included in the ban.

Bembridge Lifeboat and the Lee-on-Solent helicopter went to the aid of a Ryde fishing boat drifting in the Solent. On their way the fishing boat capsized and sank but there was no-one on board. Unable to return to her station the lifeboat sought refuge in Cowes harbour.

With no ferries running and virtually every road

Morestead Down, near Twyford where hundreds of trees fell, many of them weakened by the storm of 1987.

blocked by fallen trees, the Isle of Wight was marooned. The Downs Road from the Hare and Hounds to Brading was closed because a number of vehicles were blown over. St. Thomas' Church, Newport was sealed off as slates toppled from the roof of the parish church. In Sylvan Avenue, East Cowes, a street lamp collapsed onto the road. Children were evacuated from Totland Primary School because of the likelihood of trees falling, and two county council workmen cheated death when a 60 foot tree crashed onto their lorry, missing them by inches. At the Royal County Hospital, Ryde, 16 patients had been treated for injuries by 2.30 pm.

For Hampshire police it was the busiest day they had ever known. By 11 pm, a massive 2,334 incidents had been reported to the control room at Winchester. Hampshire Fire Brigade received more than 800 calls. Because communications were so erratic Hampshire County Council and many city councils again enlisted the help of Raynet, the Radio Amateur Emergency Network. Local radios set up help lines, passing essential information to the emergency services. Centres were set up in schools and civic centres, where hot meals were cooked. At Pennington, Bartley, Bishop's Waltham and New Alresford, 200 dinners were cooked for people unable to heat food at home.

Southern Electricity, learning from their experience of the 1987 storm, quickly called in extra engineers to work around the clock in a bid to restore power. By the weekend, 45,000 homes were reconnected to the power grid but it was more than a week before Hampshire and the Isle of Wight were back to normal.

At Gosport, storm damage forced the closure of the ferry pontoon and an emergency service to cope with the ferry's 5,000 passengers a day was organised by the Royal Clarence Yard. At Christchurch, Eileen Collins, a 70-year-old pensioner was distraught when £250 in cash was blown out of her handbag as she crossed the road. At Bournemouth, 80 guests were evacuated from the New Durley Dean Hotel after gales caused immense damage to the roof. At Hayling Island, a 200-year-old barn which was being converted into a "dream house" was just blown away. From all corners of the county came stories of heartbreak, courage and endurance.

As the winds abated, Hampshire and the Isle of Wight — for the second time in three years — were left with a "hurricane hangover", which looked as if it would take years to clear up. Farm buildings were again damaged, trees that had withstood the winds of '87, had not been able to compete with this one, Glasshouses, neatly reglazed, were shattered again. It was another great financial burden.

Morestead Road, near Winchester — just an avenue of stumps!

In the wake of the storm came the floods — and in some areas of Fareham and Gosport. three inches of raw sewage in back gardens. The M27 was waterlogged but lunatic drivers still raced along putting at risk the lives of policemen who were trying to enforce a speed limit. A spokesman said at the time: "The situation is chaotic. Drivers have completely disregarded the electronic signs showing the speed limit. There have been a large number of accidents."

Many areas of Portsmouth were under water and Hayling Island looked like a huge paddy field. Homes and garages at Lee-on-Solent had to be pumped out and serious flooding closed the Titchfield by-pass.

This time no-one labelled this storm as a "once-in-a-lifetime" affair.

Another road is opened to traffic as a large tree is removed from the Andover Road, Winchester, near the Jolly Farmers pub.

In a repeat of the 1987 storm, thousands of trees fell across hundreds of roads. This time the winds blew during the daytime.

High-sided vans and lorries stood no chance. This was the scene of the A339 near Hannington.

*Two workmen helping to restore Uppark House, South Harting were killed when a temporary
roof was lifted in the air by the winds and crashed on top them.*

The Selborne Yew, one of the oldest trees in the country had stood the test of time for more than 1,200 years. But it could not stand the test of another great wind and, almost gruesomely, toppled over, revealing human bones. The Yew was carefully pruned and lifted back into place but, sadly, it failed to grow. The picture on the left was taken in the summer of 1993.

Near this spot
lie the remains of our forbears
disturbed by the fall of the great Yew
in the gale of 25th January 1990.
Those who rebuilt this church about 1180 A.D.
may be among them.

✠

May they rest in peace

The Great Yew of Selborne, drastically pruned and still alive, was pulled back into place. A notice, among the gravestones, advertised cut timber for sale with the proceeds going to church funds. It was hoped, at the time, that there might be continued life in the ancient tree. The photographs were taken in February, 1990.

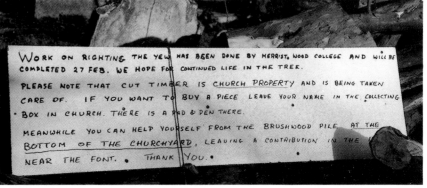

WORK ON RIGHTING THE YEW HAS BEEN DONE BY MERRIST, WOOD COLLEGE AND WILL BE COMPLETED 27 FEB. WE HOPE FOR CONTINUED LIFE IN THE TREE.

PLEASE NOTE THAT CUT TIMBER IS CHURCH PROPERTY AND IS BEING TAKEN CARE OF. IF YOU WANT TO BUY A PIECE LEAVE YOUR NAME IN THE COLLECTING BOX IN CHURCH. THERE IS A PAD & PEN THERE.

MEANWHILE YOU CAN HELP YOURSELF FROM THE BRUSHWOOD PILE AT THE BOTTOM OF THE CHURCHYARD, LEAVING A CONTRIBUTION IN THE F NEAR THE FONT. THANK YOU.

Heavy lifting gear was used to clear the trees which had fallen on houses at Packenham Road, Basingstoke, in January 1990.

At Bentley, near Alton, nearly 2.5 inches of rain fell on 3rd February, 1990. The River Wey burst its banks and turned a 20-foot wide river into a raging torrent, a quarter of a mile wide in places. One house had water rushing in the front door and out of the back.

Vigorous lows kept on coming

February, 1990

MORE floods, more gales, more stormy seas. The severe weather which had abated after the violence of late January was quick to return. On Saturday 3rd February, 1990 yet another storm swirled in from the Atlantic. This time the track of the storm centre was along the English Channel and the strongest winds hit France, leaving 23 dead. Torrential rain, with driving sleet and snow, flooded roads right across Hampshire. Again, police and fire brigade switchboards were jammed with emergency calls for help. Again roads were closed as the waters began to rise.

The constant downpour — 0.8 inches of rain in six hours — made conditions treacherous and the heavy sleet reduced visibility to nil. Police warned motorists not to leave home unless in an emergency and then only with the greatest of care. By Sunday, all the river valleys in southern England were flooded and Hampshire had soaked up four inches of rain — the equivalent of 400 tons of water tipped on to every field or estate the size of a football pitch.

In Titchfield, three cars collided on the flooded by-pass which was then closed to traffic. A Gosport and Fareham Inshore Rescue Service Landrover winched the cars out of the knee-deep water. In Marchwood, cars tried to battle through water above wheel height. In Southampton, the Town Quay area was blocked by floodwater and householders pleaded for sandbags to protect their homes. Further afield, the Severn Valley rose 14 feet above normal and Gloucestershire had its worst floods for 43 years. The little village of Upton-upon-Severn became Severn-upon-Upton!

Almost inevitably there was tragedy. On 7th February a 25-year-old Hampshire RAC patrolman, responding to an appeal for help, was killed when a large tree fell on his Sherpa van at Crawley Beeches, near Winchester. Simon Burke, from Longparish, should have been off-duty but was asked to work overtime because of the conditions.

By now, storm-force winds were again buffeting the south of England and driving rain was compounding problems, particularly in the Thames Valley. Weathermen could hardly believe what was happening. They checked their computers. Sure enough, yet another storm was closing in fast, hard on the heels of the current chaos.

The Met. Office, upset by criticisms that the BBC's weather warnings were "astonishingly inaccurate" flashed out this message: "Vigorous low will track across central southern Scotland bringing severe gales to much of UK. Southern coastal areas will be the worst affected with mean speeds up to 60 mph and gusts to 90mph. Further rain will exacerbate existing high river levels."

Hampshire and the Isle of Wight was expecting the

THE **ECHO** Fareham

SATURDAY, FEBRUARY 3, 1990   PRICE 18p

PLUS winter New homes FOR THE 90s   12 PAGE SUPPLEMENT   SEE PAGE 21

Teenager in fatal accident
A YOUNG teenage girl died when the car in which she was a passenger crashed off the Hook Road at Ampfield.
The 17-year-old, who has not been named by police, died instantly.
The Ford Fiesta collided with trees on a left hand bend just before midnight last night.
The driver of the car, an 18-year-old man received slight injuries in the accident and was taken to Southampton General Hospital. Police have issued an appeal for witnesses.

Linesman died in crash
A VICTIM of a road accident near Salisbury has been named as an emergency electricity board linesman drafted in from Scotland to help restore power to blacked-out South Wiltshire.
Mr Donald Miller, aged 52, from Hatton, Aberdeen, died when he was struck by a car on the A345 Salisbury-Amesbury road.

Driver hurt
CAR driver Samantha Winter, 18, of Crofton Way, Swanmore, was "satisfactory" at Queen Alexandra Hospital, Cosham, today after a four-vehicle crash at the village's Gravel Hill-Forest Road junction yesterday.
Other drivers, Celia Emery, 44, of Hospital Road, Shirrell Heath, John Claringbould, 25, of Cowplain, and Ian

FLOOD CHAOS HITS SOUTH

By Suzanne Dixon and Jacqui Goddard

SEVERE weather hit Hampshire hard today as torrential rain and driving sleet and snow flooded roads across the county.
Police and Hampshire Fire Brigade switchboards were jammed with emergency calls for help. Roads were closed as the waters began to rise.
The constant downpour throughout the night and morning made conditions treacherous and some areas impassable.
Heavy sleet and snow reduced visibility several hours due to the dreadful weather conditions.
A Gosport and Fareham inshore rescue Service Land-Rover, driven by Mike Allen, winched two stranded cars out of the knee-deep water.
• Traffic came to standstill at junction

TITCHFIELD: A Land-Rover winches a car clear of trouble.

Canisters washed up on beaches

THE TOUGH GET GOING

worst. Across the two counties, the army and the emergency services were standing by, on red alert. It did not happen — and this time weathermen were accused of scaremongering. One of them, Francis Wilson said: "Meteorologists had been dragged through the fortnight by a jet stream, with hardly time to draw breath. Individual extreme weather events have been handled with great skill. A tranquil spell is badly needed."

The weather gods had other ideas. By 12th February, the flood crisis was over but gale force winds returned with a vengeance. 15,000 homes suffered power cuts and weathermen warned that even stronger winds were on their way. People were advised not to walk in the New Forest or leave their vehicles in car parks because of the danger of falling trees. Sealink cancelled all services. Tree surgeons were called in to clear two 60 foot pine trees which were threatening to fall on a maternity home at Lymington. The Army were again put on standby and the people of Hampshire and the Isle of Wight braced themselves for another day of "hurricane horror", wondering if Mother Nature would ever return to a benevolent mood.

January and February, 1990 were to become two of the most notable weather months of the century and, nationally, all sorts of records were broken. The beleaguered people of southern England wondered if another wonderful summer, like that of 1989, would follow. It was almost too much to believe. No-one knew it at the time, of course, but the summer of 1990 was to be one of the hottest of the century.

The longest drought ever

1988 — 1991

AFTER the appalling weather of 1987 with floods, storms and snows and a very wet start to 1988, few people would have bet that before long drought and heat would be making the headlines. But this was exactly what happened, emphasising the Jekyll and Hyde nature of our weather and why it forms such a topic of conversation in pubs, clubs and offices.

The period 1988-1991 proved to be the warmest four year sequence for England in 332 years of temperature records. Strong sun and high temperatures led to massive evaporation and rivers which had been overflowing in January, 1988, when as much as eight inches of rain (200mm) fell, slowly began to dry up. On the Isle ofWight, 1988 was a warm year and, around the Solent, May and June together only totalled 1.6 inches (40mm) of rain and November and December were even drier. This was small consolation to crowds at Wimbledon when the men's singles' final was washed out by a deluge. Play started four and a half hours late, only to be abandoned 23 minutes later. MessrsBecker and Edberg were not amused.

After a very mild winter when Christmas Eve brought temperatures of 58F (14.4C) at Romsey, it was May, 1989 that captured the headlines with 329 hours of sunshine at Ryde and temperatures inland in Hampshire of 84F (29C). A dozen factory workers in Havant collapsed with dizziness and dehydration in the middle of a meeting to discuss the overheating in the factory. By June, Southern Water Authority were concerned about water levels being 10 per cent below average values. June through to the end of August Shide on the Isle of Wight had only recorded 3.1 inches (81mm) of rain.

The dry conditions and Mediterranean-like sunshine had a marked effect on rivers. The flow of the Itchen, a chalk river sustained mainly by groundwater percolating through the Hampshire Downs, dwindled steadily. Water was artificially pumped from the chalk to augment its flow. By mid-December the gauging station at Highbridge, near Eastleigh, registered its lowest level on record, even lower than after the blazing summer of 1976. Concern was also felt for the River Test and its valuable fishing grounds. Dwindling salmon stocks were due to the failure of landowners to rake river beds to prevent silting up of the gravel bed but also the reduced flow led to less natural scouring.

The following winter, 1989-90, again was mild, so much so that January and February's temperatures combined were the warmest generally in England in a record going back to 1659. It was also very wet, 12.4 inches (317mm) fell in this time at Vernham Dean. This had a dramatic effect on rivers. The River Itchen in February was bankfull with record flow rates. In north west Hampshire, there was a 48 foot rise in underground water levels. However, the price to pay for a wet winter was death and destruction caused by the storms which constantly lashed Britain during January and February. The worst was the tragic gale of 25th January, 1990 in which six people died in Hampshire alone (47 in UK) and total insured losses for the winter were put at £2,500 million pounds.

Suddenly the atmosphere calmed down, the pressure rose and March was warm and dry. It proved the third warmest in a record going back to 1659. Only 0.2 inches of rain (5mm) fell at Romsey. April was the sunniest on Ryde's record books, which led to May and a glorious start with brilliant sunshine and the mercury topping 82F (28C). The National Farmers' Union reported river levels lower than in 1976, the Wey in Hampshire being targeted as one of the nation's worst affected. The spectre of 1976 was beginning to stalk the countryside, for overall it was the driest Spring since 1893. There was a respite in June, though rainfall was only average, then pressure rose and at Alton there was no rainfall for 38 days from 8th July to 14th August. The high pressure became stationary to the east of Britain, wafting up hot Continental air over England. The bone-hard ground meant that the sun did not waste energy evaporating moisture from the surface. Conditions were ripe for even hotter weather. The mercury responded. Record temperatures hit the headlines and the temperature just fell short of 97F (36C) in Hampshire, a county record and a new British record was established at Cheltenham in Gloucestershire of 99F (37.2C) on 3rd August.

Records were also smashed as far as Mid Southern Water was concerned with a daily consumption of 68 million gallons in the Aldershot, Fleet and Odiham areas, 40 per cent above average. An extra 20 tons of beer had to be sent to the Isle of Wight for the Cowes Regatta and, for only the second time since the end of the Second World War, Youngs opened its brewery at the weekend to satiate demand. Six foot Caribbean turtles were seen in the Channel and a 49lb Mediterranean sunfish was caught off Cowes, the result of warmer sea conditions. Inland, Liphook, the famous hot spot, had at high noon the appearance of the dry, dusty emptiness of a wild west movie. Fires raged through heath and woodland. A massive blaze in the Alice Holt Forest closed the A31 near Bentley, causing an eight mile traffic jam. In order to beat the heat the Ordnance Survey in Southampton opened their offices at 6 am.

Inevitably, the heatwave was blamed on global

East Meon, a village renowned for its great floods of previous years was bone dry in the summer of 1990 with cracked mud on the river bed.

warming enhanced by man's pollution of the atmosphere. There was some justification for this idea, since 1990 was the warmest year in the global record with 1988, 1983 and 1987 next in line and with 1989 seventh. However, it is difficult to decide if this is just a temporary upturn or a more lasting and potentially damaging trend.

Another fairly dry autumn and winter followed and again May, 1991 raised fears of water restrictions. It was the driest May in the Christchurch Bay area this century but June and July turned out wet. August reversed the trend, being the second driest this century in some parts and December was very dry with only seven days when any rain fell. On the Isle of Wight, 1991 was the driest year since 1973. Rain continued in short supply throughout January and February and the National Rivers Authority in Hampshire experienced their lowest November-

January rainfall total since records began in 1892! Things looked very ominous as the winter recharge of the aquifers did not materialise. The pendulum swung again. The Isle of Wight had its wettest April since 1966, followed by another dry and sunny May.

It was Charles II who said that the English summer comprises three fine days and a thunderstorm. Severe storms materialised on Monday 20th July, with nearly two inches (49mm) of rain at Shanklin with the resultant floodwaters causing thousands of pounds worth of damage. It was thought by some Islanders to be the worst storm for 30 years. In Southampton 2,000 properties had lost their power supplies. Lightning gutted a house in Fareham. By the end of November Vernham Dean, near Andover, had measured 24.38 inches (619mm) in just five months. What a contrast to two years before! And February fill dyke followed. The drought appeared to be over.

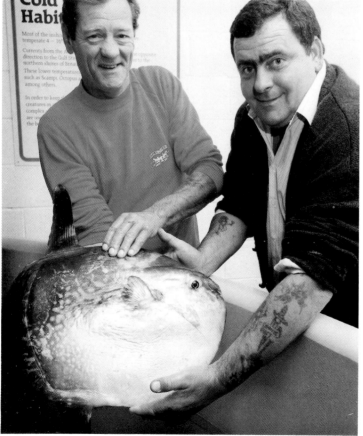

During the summers of 1989 and 1990, Hampshire and the Isle of Wight became tinder dry, straining the resources of the fire brigades who enrolled the help of the army and general public to cope with the thousands of heathland fires. Picture above shows firemen tackling a grassland blaze at Eastern Road, Portsmouth.

The sea waters, during the summer of 1990, were so warm that six-foot Caribbean turtles were seen and, off Cowes, a rare Mediterranean sunfish was caught. On the scales it weighed in at a huge 49 pounds.

Thousands of gallons of water collected in the fields and farmland of the Isle of Wight following torrential rain on 27th October, 1990. The saturated earth above the village of Brighstone could take no more and the sheer weight of the floodwater sent many acres of soil swirling through the village centre.

The village of Easton, near Winchester on 7th February, 1991. According to British Rail it was "the wrong type of snow" because it clogged up engines and disrupted services.

The heaving seas crash against the South Parade and Pier at Southsea in September, 1991.

Whirlwind

A cold front crept across Hampshire on its journey from the North-East on 19th June, 1992. When it reached Chandler's Ford there was a period of calmness before a black, ragged cloud passed overhead, accompanied by a roaring wind. This was a whirlwind. It struck 11 houses in Kent Road, Cops Row and Sussex Road. Branches were torn down and dustbin lids sent spinning. There was no thunder, or lightning or hail and the damage was confined to an area of about 50 feet in width.

Silver awards for a rescue at sea

THE morning of Sunday 25th October, 1992 was violent. Gale-force winds were blowing and waves, up to 20 feet high, were causing great distress for those unfortunate enough to be at sea. The ketch, *Donald Searle* was among them. She had anchored at the eastern end of Chichester Bar but her sails had been blown out, her engines had failed and she was dragging anchor slowly eastward. On board, the 17 crew fearing the worst, sent out a Mayday message to The Solent Coastguard.

Hayling Island lifeboatman, Frank Dunster with his own inflatable rescue boat and two crew managed to reach the scene.

Although his boat was under constant danger of capsizing he was able to take two people off the yacht before further help arrived in the shape of helmsman, Roderick James, also in his own rescue boat with two crew. They had picked their way through treacherous seas and could see the ketch being picked up and heaved bodily to leeward before returning to her original bearing. In these conditions the two lifeboat crews took a further seven from the yacht and helped the others to be winched aboard a helicopter.

For their actions that day, James and Dunster were awarded the RNLI's second highest award for bravery, the silver medal.

Under the weather and under water at The Royal Oak, Langstone Harbour.

Lifeboatmen rescue pub customers

MOUNTAINOUS waves pounded Old Portsmouth on three separate occasions during January 1993, flooding the old city and prompting irate residents to demand immediate improvements to the coastal defences. The waves, whipped up by gale-force winds, in excess of 65 mph, crashed over the sea wall into Broad Street, breached the sandbags and lapped menacingly into homes, shops and pubs.

At its peak on 10th January, the floods in Broad Street and Bath Square were three feet deep and customers of the Spice Island pub were ferried to safety by lifeboatmen using a dinghy. Residents found themselves baling water from their homes just two days after being told by the city council that improved defences were not urgently required.

Councillors explained that the circumstances were exceptional. They were right. Sea defences were breached at Havant and Lee-on-the-Solent; flood water swirled into the bar of the Royal Oak at Langstone Harbour; shops at Gosport were awash; the Haslar Bridge was under water and Titchfield residents claimed they suffered their worst flooding ever as the River Meon gushed over the water Meadows and into the village.

Coastal roads were closed, a Red Funnel ferry was blown sideways and the wind turned over light aircraft at Eastleigh. The only people to enjoy the experience was "irresponsible" windsurfers at Portchester who found the gale-force conditions and high tides "quite exhilarating".

Ferry blown off course in August gale

The Bank Holiday of 1992 was blighted by one of the windiest August days ever known. Thousands cut short their day trips or stayed at home in gales, gusting to 77 mph which were more typical of late November.

Ferry passengers faced delays of up to three hours as the heavy seas prevented ships reaching their berths. There were many anxious moments for those who did get away, including the 690 passengers and crew on the P and O ferry, *Pride of Winchester* which was blown off course while attempting to enter Portsmouth Harbour.

Further away in the Channel, nine people on board the yacht *Sena Sinoria* were rescued after it ran into difficulties. Three were taken off by helicopter and others by lifeboat, after jumping into 15 ft high seas.

During the day more than half an inch of rain fell on parts of Hampshire and flood alerts were in force on several rivers.

Much of the low-lying areras of Southampton was flooded during the violent storm of 26th May, 1993, including Milbrook Road, which this cyclist appears to be negotiating without too much trouble. However, it was another type of transport which provided the real drama on this day....

The burnt out body of the jet on the M27.

The Spanish Plume jet crash

AN executive jet was trying to land at Eastleigh Airport, Southampton during a thunderstorm on Wednesday 26th May, 1993 when it aquaplaned on the runway, ran up a bank, smashed through a fence and hit two cars on the M27. The pilot and co-pilot, the only people aboard, scrambled out of the aircraft before it exploded.

Airport fire crews had been put on standby and reached the twin-engined Cessna Citation 550 within minutes. The pilot, Albert Thompson, aged 63 and his colleague, Mr Kamran Irani, 43 both from Oxford were treated for shock and minor injuries at Southampton General Hospital. Three men in the two cars were also taken to hospital.

The incident happened during a storm which caused great damage across southern and western England. More than 40 lightning strikes were reported as landslides and flooding blocked numerous roads. Reverberating thunder claps were accompanied by three hours of torrential rain and thousands of homes were blacked out.

A spokesman for the London Weather Centre said at the time that the storm had been caused by a phenomenon known as "Spanish Plume", with a build-up of very warm air moving north east from the Bay of Biscay. The cloud tops of the storm, whose height determines the severity, reached 48,000 feet on this occasion..

ALTHOUGH the erosion of the cliffs at Barton-on-Sea has been temporarily halted, residents of Marine Drive continue to live with the fear that one great storm could send them and their homes tumbling over the edge. The same cliffhanger situation faces scores of people living near the eroding coastline around Southampton Water and Christchurch Bay. Their future is in the hands of the elements.

At Barton, many homes and businesses have simply disappeared overnight. Before a drainage system was put in place in the 1960's, the cliff was eroding at a rate of two metres a year. Since the repairs have been completed, erosion has been delayed to two metres in 18 years, but that has been enough to claim more homes.

The battle to safeguard the sea boundary, particularly the vulnerable Hampshire coastline, has been going on for years and engineers are constantly patching, replacing and dredging.

No-one however, has ever dared to guarantee a defence against the sea.

Highs and lows in Hampshire and the Isle of Wight

HOTTEST DAY

97.2F (36.2C) on
3rd August, 1990
at South Farnborough

COLDEST NIGHT

-1.9F (-18.8C) on
9th January, 1901
at Swarraton

WETTEST DAY

5.16 inches (131mm)
on 26th September,
1933 at Fleet

DRIEST YEAR

12.73 inches (323mm)
at Portchester in 1921

SUNNIEST YEAR

2,230 hours at
Shanklin in 1959

SNOWIEST YEAR

Many inland parts had
a snow cover from 27th
December to 3rd March
— a total of 67 days —
in the winter of 1962-3

DEEPEST SNOW

The Isle of Wight had
level snow around three
feet (almost a metre)
during the blizzards of
January, 1881

COLDEST WINTER

The winter of 1962-3
was the coldest
since 1740

STRONGEST WIND

104mph St Catherine's,
Isle of Wight on
16th October, 1987

WETTEST YEAR 58 inches (1,481mm) at Privett in 1951

Photographs by courtesy of:

Authors (L to R) Mark Davison, Bob Ogley and Ian Currie with The Norfolk and Suffolk Weather Book which was also published in 1993.

INDEX

Bob Ogley

BOB was a journalist for 30 years until leaving the editorship of the *Sevenoaks Chronicle* in 1989 to become a full-time publisher and author. The overnight success of his first book *In The Wake of The Hurricane*, which became a national bestseller in both editions, launched him into publishing in the nicest possible way and he has since written a further six books. In 1990 he wrote *Biggin on The Bump*, the history of the RAF fighter station at Biggin Hill, which received tremendous reviews from national, local and aviation press. The book raised £10,000 in author's royalties for the RAF Benevolent Fund. His latest effort is *Doodlebugs and Rockets - the Story of the Flying Bombs*.

Bob has raised a further £60,000 with the hurricane books for environmental charities and has discovered a supplementary career as a speaker to clubs and organisations. Recently he has teamed up with Ian Currie and Mark Davison to research, write and publish *The Kent Weather Book, The Sussex Weather Book, The Essex Weather Book, The Norfolk and Suffolk Weather Book* and now *The Hampshire and Isle of Wight Weather Book*, the sixth of a popular county weather series.

Ian Currie

THE ever-changing moods and patterns in our weather have always fascinated Ian Currie. He has vivid childhood memories of the 1958 thunderstorm and the deep winter snows of 1962-63, living then near Chislehurst in Kent. Sharing his interest with others has always been a feature of Ian's life. He writes a weekly weather column for several newspapers as well as being a weatherman for Radio Mercury and County Sound.

A graduate of Geography and Earth Science and teacher for 20 years, Ian is now a full-time writer and speaker to clubs and societies all over South-East England. He is a Fellow of the Royal Meteorological Society and a member of the Climatological Observers Link. Together with Mark Davison he has written *Surrey in The Hurricane, London's Hurricane* and *The Surrey Weather Book.* and *Red Sky at Night -Weather Sayings For All Seasons.* Ian also wrote the *I Spy Weather Book*

Mark Davison

MARK has been in local journalism for 15 years and is currently deputy editor of the *Surrey Mirror Series*. He is co-author of six county books on weather events and has shown a keen interest in the climate since the big freeze of 1962-3 when, as a small child, he was spell-bound by the heavy falls of snow. In January 1987 his interest was totally renewed.

Risking whatever the elements might try and throw at him, he has ventured out on many wild nights to gather first-hand accounts of the South East's storms and freezes. Together with Ian Currie he has produced a set of postcards commemorating the severe cold spell in February, 1991.

Froglets books

In The Wake of The Hurricane
(National Edition Hardback)
ISBN 0 9513019 4 2......................................£9.95

Surrey in The Hurricane
ISBN 0 9513019 2 6......................................£7.50

London's Hurricane
(Paperback) ISBN 0 9513019 3 4.................£4.95
(Hardback) ISBN 0 9513019 8 5.................£7.95

Eye on The Hurricane
(Eastern Counties)
(Paperback) ISBN 0 9513019 6 9.................£7.95
(Hardback) ISBN 0 9513019 7 7.................£11.95

King Oak of Sevenoaks
(A children's story)
ISBN 1 8723370 0 7 ....£6.95

Biggin On The Bump (The most famous fighter station in the world).
(Paperback) ISBN 1 872337 05 8.................£9.50
(Hardback) ISBN 1 872337 10 4...............£14.95

The Surrey Weather Book
Published by Frosted Earth
ISBN 0 9516710 1 4....................................£7.50

The Sussex Weather Book
ISBN 1 872337 30 9...................................£9.95

The Kent Weather Book
ISBN 1 872337 35 X...................................£9.95

The Norfolk and Suffolk Weather Book
Paperback ISBN 1 872337 99 6....................£9.95
Hardback ISBN 1 872337 98 8...................£16.95

The Essex Weather Book
ISBN 1 872337 66 X................................£9.95

Doodlebugs and Rockets (The Battle of the Flying Bombs)
(Hardback) ISBN 1 872337 22 8...............£16.95
(Paperback) ISBN 1 872337 21 X..............£9.95

Red Sky at Night
Published by Frosted Earth
ISBN 9516710 2 2....................................£4.95

To order any one of these books, please note that our address is **Froglets Publications, Brasted Chart, Westerham, Kent TN16 ILY.** TELEPHONE **0959 562972** FAX **0959 565365**